100+ STEAM ACTIVITIES

KIDS WON'T LEARN IN SCHOOL!

D1592237

POPULAR MECHANICS

© 2021 by Hearst Magazine Media, Inc.

Book Design by Gillian MacLeod
Cover Photographed by Philip Friedman
Cover Styled by Miako Katoh

ISBN: 978-1-950099-98-6

HEARST

100+ STEAM ACTIVITIES
KIDS WON'T LEARN IN SCHOOL!

POPULAR
MECHANICS

Table of Contents

Introduction to the Maker Mindset 6

Chapter 1

STEAM Basics 11

Jell-O Eyes 12

Summer Creature Identification 15

Bird-Watching 16

Glitter Slime 21

Plants' Defense Mechanisms 22

Terrarium 25

Cricket Sounds Thermometer 26

The Ideal Temperature for Hot Chocolate 27

Thunderstorm Predictors 28

Weather Station 31

Wind Turbine 32

Zipline 34

One Light, Three Switches 36

DNA Recipe 37

LED Art 39

Squishy Circuits 40

3D Bioluminescence Art 43

Pumpkin-Carving Like A Pro 44

Camouflage 49

Map and Compass 50

Constellation Mapping 53

Rock-Paper-Scissors Riddle 56

The Locker Prank 57

The Perfect Field Goal 58

The Perfect Knuckleball 60

Chromatography in Leaves 62

Icy Adventures 65

Mathematical Life Skills 66

The Best Way to Cut a Sandwich 69

Detergent Bottle Ukulele 70

Gift-Wrapping Trick 74

Upcycled Art 77

The Absolute Best Way to Eat an Oreo®, According to Science 80

Candy Dispenser 82

Canning Strawberry Jam Preserves 87

Stilts 88

Wind-Up Dragster 91

Rolling Comeback Can 93

Backyard Water Rocket 94

Floating Ping-Pong Table 97

Hot-Air Balloon Simulator 98

A Wind-Powered Boat 101

The Lowdown on Dams 103

The Perfect Paper Airplane 106

HEADS UP!

Keep an eye out for this symbol. These activities should be performed with an adult.

Adult Supervision Required!

Chapter 2

Building on that Maker Mindset 109

Monster Mask 110

Your Own Bird's Nest 113

Book Light 114

Ice Lantern 117

Your Own Emoji Language 118

Battle Bots 121

Coded Hidden Treasure 122

Water Balloon Launcher 125

Ping-Pong Cannon 126

A Backyard Bike Wash 131

Unstoppable Airplane Launcher 132

Ice Cream Maker 137

Noodle Art 140

Artwork Digitization 142

Sandcastle Architecture 144

Empire Planning 146

Onager Catapult 149

Basketball Catapult 152

Backyard Slip n Slide 157

Sand Pendulum 158

Ball Toss 161

Matchbox Car Belt 162

Solar-Powered Night-Light 165

Time Capsule 168

Periscope 171

Pipe Chime 172

Boot-Box Boombox 175

Mars Rover 178

Chapter 3

Putting It All Together 183

Electronic Fruit Clock 184

Secret Message Transporter Machine 186

Camping Setup Like a Pro 190

Rube Goldberg Machine 197

Robot Scribbler 200

Air Hockey Table 204

Steerable Sled 208

Marble Run 212

Six Things to Remember Now That You're Done! 216

Solutions 218

Credits 221

Introduction to the Maker Mindset

Before you dive in, get
to know what makes makers
and STEAM great!

You Are a Maker

Yes, you! Even if you haven't *technically* invented anything yet. Just think about these questions:

Do you like to take things apart and see if you can use them for something else?

Have you ever built a structure out of playing cards or pizza boxes?

Do you like coding and robotics?

Do you like digital storytelling using a green screen and computer?

Have you thought about ways to make your bike faster?

Do you jump at the chance to try virtual reality?

Are 3D printing projects your favorite, or do you love using circuitry to enhance technology?

Do you have aspirations of becoming an engineer who makes life better with your inventions?

Is your school's maker space your favorite space?

If you answered yes to any of these, you are made of the stuff of makers! And you're made of that stuff even if you answered no. Being a maker is all about your mindset, not what you know or what you've done!

A Peek Into the Maker Mindset

We are ALL makers. We ALL have the ability to inspire new innovative projects that could change the world. Think about this; the Internet wasn't designed overnight. Your life-altering invention won't be either. Makers ask a lot of questions, like:

What does the world need? What problems do we need to fix?

What speaks to me?

Do I have the right materials?

Do I have the right tools?

Did this idea work or should I scrap it and start over?

Makers use the engineering design process (more on that later!) to tackle projects. They fail forward with a positive attitude and a growth mindset. Remember: It's OK to say an idea didn't pan out. Just don't let your frustration keep you from seeing what isn't there yet. Take a break and get a new perspective. Take a step back. Examine your tools. Explore your materials. Evaluate your research. You may be surprised at what you discover.

How Do STEAM Activities Inspire Future Makers?

Makers solve problems. To do that, you need STEAM, the integration of science, technology, engineering, art, and math. Try using all of them to become the best maker! Here's how.

Science

The science of making involves observation, data collection, and citing evidence while asking a lot of questions! To become an experienced maker, you need to experiment and study the physical and natural world.

Technology

To make your prototypes more innovative, consider integrating more technology. Tech like computer programs, circuitry, and robotics can help you test your inventions in new ways, all while building on the knowledge you applied from the science category.

Engineering

Use the engineering design process to foster a maker mindset and give your ideas wings. It shows you how various tools and materials can be used in different combinations to create something new, which is what tinkering is all about!

Art

Design can be just as important as the final product if it serves a clear purpose. Art, whether in the form of blueprints or sketches, allows makers to envision possible solutions to new inventions while keeping them grounded in what is actually possible.

Math

Math can help makers figure out if an invention can actually succeed. What causes huge system failures? Doing the math in various trials may ultimately lead you to the correct solution.

Now, put that maker mindset to work! Know your tools and materials and do research to comprehend their full potential for your projects. For example, know your conductors and insulators and how to make closed circuits before starting an electricity project. Know how to build an algorithm and use loops, conditionals, and if/else statements before you start writing a new computer program. Showing passion for your craft will enhance your ability to make and innovate!

The Engineering Design Process

Next, use the engineering design process when working through a project.

Step 1

Define the Problem

Write down what you know about the problem and what research you need to do. Show empathy by understanding what people need and why they need it. It'll go a long way in engineering a solution to real-world problems.

Step 2

Brainstorm Ideas and Solutions

Now, write down how you could solve the problem. Note potential obstacles, like limited time or materials. Research what solutions have already been invented, and find a way to make yours even better.

Step 3

Select the Best Option After Exploring Your Ideas

Begin by sketching a drawing on graph paper, making a blueprint, generating a list of materials and steps, or engineering a 3D model on a computer. Then pick which design has the best function and form.

Step 4

Build a Prototype of Your Solution

Grab the parts and pieces you need to create the first-ever [insert your brilliant invention here]! A prototype doesn't need to be perfect. It is a way to test your idea to see if it actually works!

Step 5

Test and Improve Your Prototype

Use your invention. Write down what did and did not work. Get feedback from a friend. Adjust your prototype based on what you learn.

Step 6

Share Your Solution with the World!

Use your voice. Share it. Believe in it. Anything is possible! Become a global citizen who makes the world better. Trust in the science, technology, engineering, art, and math skills that will bring your inventions to life! Have fun!

The engineering design process is a cycle. You may need to loop back to step 1 (or another step) to see where the prototype stopped working efficiently. Is there a problem in the materials, tools, science, technology, artistic design, or math?

Mary Gruber
LIBRARY MEDIA SPECIALIST
DIGITAL LITERACY DEPARTMENT HEAD AND INSTRUCTIONAL COACH
CALYPSO & FREEMANSBURG ELEMENTARY SCHOOLS
BETHLEHEM AREA SCHOOL DISTRICT

CHAPTER 1

STEAM Basics

Build a good STEAM foundation
while having fun at the same time!
Are you ready? Let's go!

TRY IT!
Jell-O Eyes

Let Jell-O show you how refraction works. This experiment uses lasers, which can be dangerous if you look directly at them, so get an adult to help.

Why It Matters

You see things—a tennis ball flying at your racket, a lion at the zoo, a funny video—because your eye is absorbing the light in front of it. When light passes through the cornea of your eye, its curved surface bends and refracts the rays. Retina tissue in the back of your eye creates a clear focal point. Your pupil increases or decreases in size to adjust so the right amount of light comes in based on the conditions. Using this science, you can understand how your optic nerve signals the brain to transform the image so you can recognize it.

What You'll Need

1 box red Jell-O

1 square baking dish

1 round ice cube mold

1 sharp knife with a smooth blade

Plate or graph paper (optional)

2 or 3 red laser pointers
Note: It's important that the laser color matches the color of the Jell-O. Otherwise, the light will not show up clearly.

1. Mix the Jell-O according to the box's instructions. Pour half into a square baking dish and the other half into your round mold. Put into the refrigerator for two to four hours.

2. Take the Jell-O from the baking dish and use the knife to cut out a 2 x 2-inch square. Put it on a plate or a piece of graph paper.

3. Point a laser so it hits the Jell-O at a 45-degree angle. What happens to the beam of light as it passes through the Jell-O? What if you change the angle of the laser?

4. Cut the rest of the Jell-O square into different shapes and notice how the laser refracts differently when it hits the new shapes. Try shining two lasers into the Jell-O from different angles at the same time and see what happens.

5. Place the sphere of Jell-O on a plate or a sheet of graph paper. Shine one laser through it. What happens to the beam of light? Try it with two or three lasers from different angles at the same time.

6. Eat the rest of the Jell-O!

Just like you would have to walk more slowly to get through deep snow, light moves more slowly through denser materials. When the laser hits the Jell-O, it slows down, shifting its direction slightly and bending the laser line.

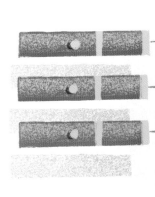

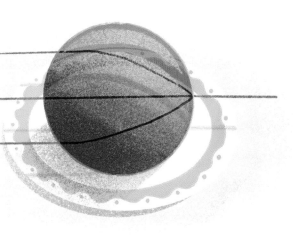

Because a sphere is perfectly round, laser beams from multiple angles will be shifted to a single point. That's exactly what's happening inside your eye when light hits it!

TRY IT!

Summer Creature Identification

Here's what you should know about the different animals that may show up in your backyard when temperatures rise.

Why It Matters

When spring arrives, many animals emerge from their long winter naps. By summer, even more animals come out, including those that migrated south for the winter. Use the field guide below to familiarize yourself with their habits and habitat so you know where to find them. Sharpening your scientific observation skills is a maker essential.

Bats

WHERE YOU'LL SEE THEM
In forested areas near lakes, ponds, and rivers

WHEN TO LOOK At dusk and for two to three hours after and before dawn

Seeing bats swooping around in summer may feel a little creepy, but the fuzzy flyers are very helpful: A bat eats its weight in insects every day, cutting down on pesky mosquitoes and other biting bugs. The most common type of bat in the United States is the little brown bat, about the size of a large mouse with wings. Like all bats, the little brown bat uses echolocation to "see" in the dark, which means it makes special calls and uses the echo to figure out its surroundings.

Snakes

WHERE YOU'LL SEE THEM
Basking in the sun on stones or in your driveway, or hiding in dark, cool places like under the deck and rocks

WHEN TO LOOK In the morning to see them sunbathing, hiding in the dark in the evening

Snakes are much less active in the winter, so you might notice more of these slithery fellows in the summer. One of the most common snakes in the United States is the garter snake. It comes in many different colors but usually has three stripes—one down the middle of its back and one on each side. Because snakes are cold-blooded, they'll sometimes sun themselves on rocks to take in heat and get energy. More often they'll be found in shady spots, where they stay to avoid getting overheated and to find prey like worms and small amphibians.

Fireflies

WHERE YOU'LL SEE THEM
Forests and fields, especially those with long grass

WHEN TO LOOK The warmest nights in May, June, and July

The lower part of a firefly's abdomen lights up because of a chemical reaction called bioluminescence. Different species flash at different times and for different reasons. Some light up as a warning to predators to signal that they have a chemical in them that tastes bad. Another species lights up to tell other fireflies whether they're male or female or if they're looking for a mate. If you live in the eastern United States, the male fireflies are the ones you see flashing in the air. West of Kansas, the female fireflies light up, but they're usually on the ground.

Hummingbirds

WHERE YOU'LL SEE THEM
In your backyard near brightly colored flowers (especially red and pink ones)

WHEN TO LOOK During the day, especially in the end of May and the beginning of June

In the summertime, hummingbirds migrate around the United States in order to find flowers, whose nectar they drink for food. They're small, but super-powerful. They're the only birds in the world that are able to hover in place or fly backward. They can do this because they flap their wings so fast—as many as 200 times per second. Their wings inspired their name: Hummingbirds' wings flap so fast, they make a low humming sound.

TRY IT!
Bird-Watching

Impress people with your knowledge of all the different kinds of birds native to your area!

Why It Matters

Birds are resilient, adaptable creatures, and learning about them will help build your maker mindset. Using your science skills, observe closely and jot down your discoveries. Do some research to validate your data and help you label, identify, and classify birds. By the time you are finished, you will have an extensive field guide whenever you need one!

Get the Gear. You don't need a powerful pair of binoculars. Pick one with a magnification between six and nine. More than that and it becomes hard to stabilize the image. The diameter of the objective lens (the end of the binoculars) determines how much light is let in. Find something between 40mm and 45mm.

Load Up Your Notebook. Do some research and write down the kinds of birds most commonly found in your area. Get detailed—jot down their size, the color of their feathers, what they sound like, and any other distinctive characteristics. This will serve as an initial field guide.

Go Outside. Your backyard may be fine for robins, but a nearby state park will have many more bird varieties. If you're a complete novice, sign up for a guided outing.

If you're on your own, spend some time in one place and let the birds come to you.

Identify That Bird! When you see a bird, note its proportions and shape. Later you'll use this information, along with your field guide, to figure out the genus or family.

If the bird is singing, try to remember the length and cadence of its song. Note behavior (i.e., whether it's hopping around on the ground or flying from branch to branch). If it's large and circling you with four to five friends overhead, you've probably been out too long and should think about heading in.

Note any distinctive marks, like a bright red head or orange breast. These are more useful than general color.

Pull Out Your Field Guide. Once you've located the proper family, use the field markings and behavior to make an ID. Don't forget to celebrate, especially when you find a rare one!

TIP

Your best chance at seeing the most species is in areas at the edges of different habitat types, like the woods near a clearing or along the shore of a river or pond. Prime times are from dawn until about 11 a.m., when the birds are up with the sun and feeding, and again at dusk.

Birds as Teachers

Birds have contributed a lot to modern-day technology. In flight, they look so elegant and effortless, which is why researchers study them in detail to improve airplane and drone design. How they build their nests has also become an engineering and architectural marvel, using materials to create a sturdy structure designed to keep the elements and predators out.

FUN FACT

Scientists discovered a rare rose-breasted grosbeak, which displays an even split down the middle between male and female coloring, leading researchers to label it a "unicorn." Keep an eye out for them!

COLOR IT!

Chapter 1

MAKE IT!
Glitter Slime

Slime isn't just fun to play with—it can also help save lives!

Why It Matters

Currently, the United States Navy is developing synthetic slime, inspired by the real-life hagfish, which is known to fill its potential attackers' mouths and gills with goo. When the slime comes in contact with sea water, it swells up to 10,000 times its initial volume in a matter of seconds. Imagine all the good ways this new type of slime can be used —fire protection from oil spills, a spray to keep sharks away, maybe even as a way to stop a bullet in its tracks! How about we try making our own—with glitter, perhaps?

What You'll Need

Large bowl

½ cup warm water

⅔ cup transparent craft glue

½ teaspoon baking soda

Colored glitter

Saline solution that contains sodium borate and boric acid

Confetti (choose a shape)

How It Works

Glue is a polymer that is activated when mixed with the borate ions in the saline solution. A chemical reaction, called cross-linking, occurs and rubbery slime is created. The baking soda helps give the slime a thicker consistency.

1. In a large bowl, mix together the water, transparent craft glue, and baking soda .

2. Add a teaspoon (or two) of glitter, and mix.

3. Stir in small squirts of saline solution, mixing well until the slime doesn't stick to your hands.

4. Add in a handful of confetti and more glitter (if desired).

5. Gently mix the slime together and knead it through your hands to play.

Take It One Step Further

Experiment with other materials. Try adding small toys that are lightweight enough to stick to the slime and stay in the mixture. Make it glow with glow-in-the-dark glue or poster paint.

TIP

If you want to deepen the perspective, depth, or artistic shape, add confetti of different colors and sizes.

Plants' Defense Mechanisms

Get to know the thorny side of nature.

Why It Matters

As a human being, your defense mechanism is most likely triggered by an internal response to fear and danger. Plants, on the other hand, have evolved all sorts of wickedly clever defense mechanisms, like thorns, prickles, and spines. While it's worth steering clear of them, many have used them as an elegant solution to home security.

A Field Guide to Thorny Plants

1. HOLLY

When you think of holly, you're certain to conjure images of the plant's evergreen leaves and red fruit, but do you consider its thorns? Each of the leathery leaves has three to five spines along its sides. They alternate in direction, with some spines pointing upward and some downward. Meanwhile, the highest branches of mature holly trees completely lack the sharp appendages.

2. ROSE

Whatever type you grow—garden, climbing, ground cover—you'll get a beautiful flowering plant with all the thorns to boot. As you've likely experienced before, roses draw blood, and they enjoy it.

3. AGAVE

Agave is a category of plants that includes many species of succulents that live in hot and dry conditions. These plants have adapted to their desert homes with various features, including spikes. In this case, the spikes poke out at predators to keep them from using the leaves as a water source. The spikes are so strong and sharp, in fact, that women in ancient Mexico were known to use them as sewing needles.

4. BOUGAINVILLEA

A fast-growing shrubby vine that can grow 40 feet long, bougainvillea uses its thorny stems to support itself on nearby plants or structures. The colorful display is actually made up of large, papery bracts that surround the tiny flowers. You definitely don't want this plant's sap to touch your skin.

5. CROWN OF THORNS

This climbing shrub grows 3 to 5 feet high and sends heavily armed branches in every direction. Originally from Madagascar, it usually needs support and looks for other plants or a fence to hold it up. Its crimson summer flowers are deceptively beautiful with dangerous thorns that lie beneath.

True or False

1. Roses enjoy drawing blood.

2. The thorns on a holly bush all point in the same direction.

3. Agave plants thrive in desert regions and use their spikes to prevent predators from stealing the water source in their leaves.

4. Bougainvillea sap won't harm you; it will just leave a sticky mess.

5. The Crown of Thorns uses other plants as support structures.

Answers on page 218

What You'll Need

Clear glass container

Rocks (polished pebbles, sea glass, marbles, etc.)

Sphagnum or sheet moss

Soil

Plants that won't overgrow the container, such as boxwood, croton, Joseph's coat, pineapple verbena, and twiggy spikemoss for sun-loving plants, and gnome ivy, golden club moss, Irish or Scottish club moss, and miniature ferns for shade-loving plants

Basic tools, including spoons or a funnel for placing soil in the container, long tweezers for positioning materials and plants, scissors for snipping greenery, and paper towels or cotton swabs for cleaning the glass

MAKE IT!
Terrarium

If you like to play in the dirt, this is the activity for you!

Why It Matters

Gardening is not as easy as it looks. Plants need water and sunlight to thrive, which is why terrariums are a great fuss-free maintenance option for gardeners who lack outdoor space: The soil and plants release water vapor that is then reused as it drips back down the glass into the soil, and the glass container helps it soak up the sun's rays when placed by a window. Here's how you can make one.

Choose a Glass Container. It can be anything from a clean, reused pickle jar to a vintage vase. Pick one with an opening wide enough to fit your hand. Just make sure the glass is clear; colored glass tends to make it difficult for plants to grow.

Pick Your Rocks. Put a handful of polished rocks or marbles in the bottom of the container. This helps to shape the terrain while helping drainage and aeration. Vary the layer's thickness by the size of the container. The smaller the vessel, the thinner the rock layer. Leave enough "head room" at the top of the terrarium so things don't look cramped.

Place Your Next Layer. Soak dried sphagnum or sheet moss in water for a few seconds and squeeze out any excess liquid. Place the slightly damp moss onto the rocks, patting it down so that it fills the entire surface area and forms a barrier that keeps the soil from sifting down into the rocks.

Add the Soil. Scoop the soil into a funnel and fill the container with several inches of soil. The greenery you'll be planting will determine the type of soil you use. For moss, use a peat moss mixture because it is less likely to mold. For other plants, non-moisture-control potting mix should work. If a plant's nursery tag indicates that it needs a specific type of soil, use that type.

Keep in mind that this layer doesn't have to be perfectly flat. Hills and valleys give the terrarium's landscape character. Again, don't fill the container too high with soil, because you'll want to have enough room for the greenery to grow.

Plant Your Plants. If you're using moss that you snagged from nature, make sure to first give it a blast of pesticide to debug it. Use scissors to trim it into shape, place it into the container, and then press it down firmly to eliminate any air pockets. For other plants, plant them as you would in an outdoor garden. Loosen the root balls, place them in a shallow layer of soil, add soil around them, and pat down the soil.

Give Them Water. Lightly water your plants to help prevent transplant shock, keeping in mind that the container doesn't have any drainage holes.

Keep Them Alive. For moss terrariums, a light misting of water every two to four weeks should suffice. For plant terrariums, heed watering instructions on the plant's nursery tag. Just be careful not to over-water.

TRY IT!

Cricket Sounds Thermometer

The sound of crickets chirping isn't just peaceful—it helps you determine temperature too!

Why It Matters

Crickets are cold-blooded. As the temperature warms up, it becomes easier for their muscles to move. The warmer they get, the more frequently they can rub the tops of their wings together, making that familiar chirping sound.

There's an easy way to figure out the temperature outside (other than looking on a weather app): Count the number of chirps crickets make in 15 seconds, then add 37 to get the temperature in Fahrenheit.

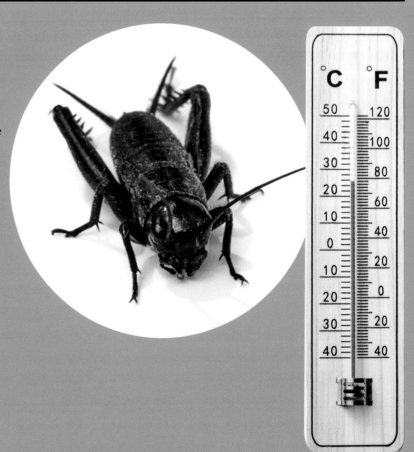

The Ideal Temperature for Hot Chocolate

Enjoy your hot cocoa without scalding your tongue.

Why It Matters

There's nothing better than a cup of hot cocoa after an afternoon sledding down the snowiest hill in the neighborhood. The only problem? It's too hot. Do the math to determine how long you need to wait until it's cooled to the perfect drinking temperature! How quickly your cocoa cools depends on the relationship between energy, heat, and temperature.

The Scene

Your cup of hot chocolate is served at 194 degrees and your hot chocolate shop's room temperature is 66 degrees.

The last number you need is the half-life—the time it takes, in any situation, for the temperature to be divided by two—based on the liquid, cup, and type of beverage. For this situation, it's 2 minutes. How do you get to a perfectly safe temperature for drinking your hot chocolate?

The Formula

194°F	—	66°F	=	_____
Serving Temperature		Room Temperature		Temperature Difference

128°F	/	2	=	_____
Temperature Difference		Minutes		Half-life

66°F	+	_____	=	_____
Room Temperature		Half-life		Hot cocoa temperature after 2 minutes

DRINK UP!

Studies have shown that the perfectly safe temperature for drinking is about 136 degrees Fahrenheit.

Did you get to a safe drinking temperature? **Answers on page 218**

TRY IT!
Thunderstorm Predictors

There's no need to fear the loud boom of thunder. Storms are more surprising than scary, so brace yourself and know when to expect them.

Why It Matters

Thunder is a result of lightning—so any time you hear it, you should be in a shelter such as a house or car. A bolt of lightning heats the air around it to 50,000 degrees. As the lightning flashes, the hot air instantly expands in every direction, causing a shock wave: thunder. If you're close to the lightning, you'll hear a loud and sharp crack. Farther away, it's more of a rumble as the sound travels and bounces off the ground, buildings, and the atmosphere. While you can see lightning from as far as 100 miles away, thunder travels only 10 to 15 miles before dissipating. Use math and science to predict how far away the next thunderstorm is in real time.

1. Make sure you're in a safe location before you begin counting. Lightning strikes the ground and anything that can conduct electricity, especially metal. Steer clear!

2. Wait for a flash of lightning.

3. Once you see it, begin counting with a rhythm of a standard clock. Keep counting until you hear a thunder clap. Then stop. How many seconds did you count?

4. Take that number and divide it by five. The answer will tell you how many miles the lightning is from your location.

Example:
5 seconds = 1 mile,
10 seconds = 2 miles,
15 seconds = 3 miles, and so on.

FUN FACT

The longest reported duration of a single lightning flash happened in Argentina on March 4, 2019. It lasted for 16.73 seconds.

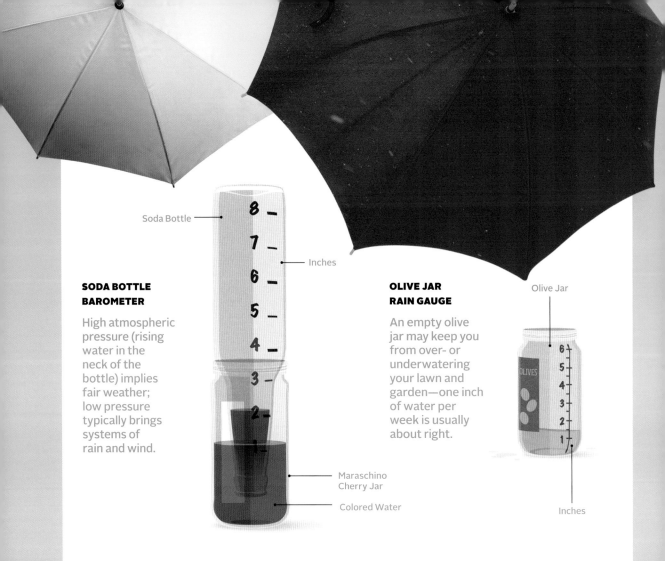

SODA BOTTLE BAROMETER

High atmospheric pressure (rising water in the neck of the bottle) implies fair weather; low pressure typically brings systems of rain and wind.

Soda Bottle

Inches

Maraschino Cherry Jar

Colored Water

OLIVE JAR RAIN GAUGE

An empty olive jar may keep you from over- or underwatering your lawn and garden—one inch of water per week is usually about right.

Olive Jar

Inches

ALUMINUM CAN WIND VANE

If the arrow (cut from a soda can or pie plate) is pointing east, the wind is coming from the east. Drastic shifts in direction may signal bad weather.

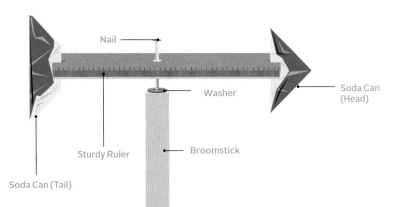

Nail

Soda Can (Head)

Washer

Sturdy Ruler

Broomstick

Soda Can (Tail)

Weather Station

Anyone can be a weather forecaster—yes, even you!

Why It Matters

You don't need a TV weather forecaster to tell you what's happening in your own backyard. With just a few items you probably already have at home, you can build a simple barometer, wind vane, and rain gauge—three key devices that help you understand the science behind how storm predictions are made. Keep an eye on the sky, and record the data. Tracking local conditions can alert you to the approach of storms or clear bluebird days. Soon, the whole neighborhood will see you as the new weather forecaster of your area!

What You'll Need

Straight-necked bottle of soda

A short, wide-mouthed jar (like that of a Maraschino cherry jar)

Food coloring

Water

Scissors

Soda can or pie plate

Ruler

Hot glue

Broomstick

Washer

Tall, wide jar (like an olive jar)

Marker

Soda Bottle Barometer

Overturn an empty straight-necked bottle of soda into a short, wide-mouthed jar. The mouth of the bottle should not reach the bottom of the jar. Starting from the mouth, mark every inch and half-inch increment. Add food coloring to some water; pour enough into the jar to cover three-quarters of the bottle neck. The water in the neck will rise when atmospheric pressure is high and sink when a low-pressure weather system approaches.

Aluminum Can Wind Vane

Cut a triangle and a trapezoid out of a soda can or pie plate to make the arrow's head and tail. Fasten the flattened pieces to the ends of a sturdy ruler by cutting thin slits into both ends of the ruler and gluing the shapes into place. Nail the ruler to a broomstick using a washer in between to allow the ruler to move smoothly. Affix the entire thing to a fence post or porch railing.

Olive Jar Rain Gauge

Empty a tall, wide jar. Starting from the base, mark every half-inch and inch increment. Place it away from overhanging branches to get valid results.

Wind Turbine

Learn how to capture the airstream's gusting force with this rugged PVC turbine design.

Why It Matters

Using wind energy, you can power up just about anything, even your cell phone! This alternative energy source may provide you with a new form of electricity for your household items. It's stronger and more efficient than pure solar energy since it can be captured both day and night as long as there is wind to generate it. Get ready to be blown away!

Build the Rotor & Nacelle

1. Insert the 2-inch piece of PVC pipe into a 90-degree fitting.

2. Slide the PVC coupler over the 2-inch pipe, forming one solid piece called the nacelle.

3. Wrap a ½-inch-wide by 18-inch-long piece of duct tape around the perimeter of the motor. This will help it fit securely in the coupler.

4. Thread the wires attached to the DC motor into the mouth of the coupler, all the way through the 90-degree PVC fitting.

5. The motor should rest snuggly in the coupler but not be pushed all the way in.

6. Next, attach the crimping hub to the motor by pressing it into the driveshaft.

7. Make sure the face of the motor is flush with the edge of the pipe.

Build the Base

1. Using four 90-degree PVC fittings, two PVC tees, and four 6-inch PVC pipe sections, construct the two sides of the turbine base.

2. Insert a 6-inch pipe into one end of the 90-degree fitting. On the opposite end of the 6-inch pipe, fit a PVC tee, followed by another 6-inch pipe and 90-degree fitting. Repeat to make the second leg of the base.

3. Drill a small hole on the bottom of the last PVC tee.

4. Connect the legs of the base by inserting the two remaining 6-inch PVC pipes into the PVC of each leg. Join the base legs via the drilled PVC tee.

Attach the Tower

1. Snake the motor's wires down the 24-inch PVC pipe; this long section is the tower.

What You'll Need

5 PVC 90-degree fittings (1-inch-diameter)

3 PVC tee fittings (1-inch-diameter)

1 PVC coupler (1-inch-diameter)

6 PVC 6-inch-long pipes (1-inch-diameter)

1 PVC 24-inch-long pipe (1-inch-diameter)

1 PVC 2-inch-long pipe (1-inch-diameter)

2 alligator clips

Poster board for blades

20-inch box fan or other wind source

Duct tape

Hot glue/glue gun

Wire cutters

Drill

KidWind Basic Turbine Building Parts Kit (includes DC motor with wires, 12-hole crimping hub, and 25 dowels; available at store.kidwind.org)

Multimeter

5mm LED bulb

Sound & Light Board

2. Attach the nacelle to the top of the tower; tap it into place so that it fits securely.

3. Thread the wires through the center PVC tee and out the drilled hole at the base of the tower.

4. Secure the tower to the tee.

5. Attach alligator clips to exposed wires.

Make the Blades

1. Create the blades from material 6 inches to 10 inches in diameter. We use poster board but you can use any stiff light material, such as a sturdy paper plate or sheets of balsa. (Note: The voltage that your turbine produces depends on the torque and RPM of the blades. We found that a configuration of two or four blades generated plenty of energy, but feel free to experiment!)

2. Secure the blades to the dowels with tape or hot glue.

3. Insert the dowels into the crimping-hub holes. Tighten the hub after inserting.

Put the Generator to Work

1. Position your turbine in front of a box fan so that the wind turns the blades; this will generate electricity.

2. Use the alligator clips to connect to a multimeter to measure the voltage. (You'll need approximately 2 volts.)

3. Once your blades are generating power, you can connect the wires of the LED bulb or the Sound & Light Board using the alligator clips.

Dowels

DC Motor

Nacelle

Tower

Crimping Hub

Pvc Coupler

Base

MAKE IT!
Zipline

Take your toys on a wild ride with this activity.

Why It Matters

Ziplines are fun, but they also serve a real purpose. They've been used to transport items down a line or as a way to travel over rivers or mountains. With a little science, particularly physics, and some math, you will be zipping objects around your home in no time!

---

1. Think About Location. Will you build it between trees in your backyard or between chair legs in your dining room? Maybe find space in the garage?

2. Consider Materials. What is it you wish to carry on the zipline and why? Will you use toy people or maybe transport secret messages from a treehouse to a ground shelter?

3. Sketch Out Your Ideas. Use graph paper and engage the engineering design process to guide your work. Remember: The speed at which you travel will be determined by several factors.

4. Start Building. Once you determine how high or low and how long or short your zipline will be, attach the ends to the proper heights and objects. Adjust the tension of the line to suit your needs.

5. Create a Carrier and Add Your Load. Will you use a basket? Maybe it needs to be waterproof with a lid? Is there enough weight to keep the object from flying out on its journey? Maybe more than one connector handle will make it sturdier.

6. Figure Out Your Braking Mechanism. Maybe taper the line at the end to adjust the slope and slow down your load? Will you use a stopper, and will it be enough to not break what you're transporting?

Zip Away!

Perhaps a fishing line or crafting wire might work best. Remember that you need to reduce friction, so ropes and cables with ridges might help decrease speed and increase resistance. Also, make sure to have about five to eight feet between points to watch your load make its way to the bottom for more than a second or two.

SOLVE IT!

One Light, Three Switches

Here's a problem that seems complicated, but you got this!

Why It Matters

It's amazing how power lines bring electricity to our homes from a larger power plant. Once the electricity is available to use, how do you know which switches will change your closed circuits to open ones? To answer that question, we have to delve into a little science, specifically circuitry. Can you solve this riddle with a little research? Remember: A light switch stops the flow of electricity, creating an open circuit.

Problem

There is a lightbulb inside a closet. The door is closed and you cannot see if the light is on or off through the door. However, you know the light is off to start. Outside of the closet, there are three light switches. One of the switches controls the lightbulb in the closet. You can flip the switches however you want, but once you open the door, you can no longer touch the switches.

How do you figure out without a doubt which switch controls the light?

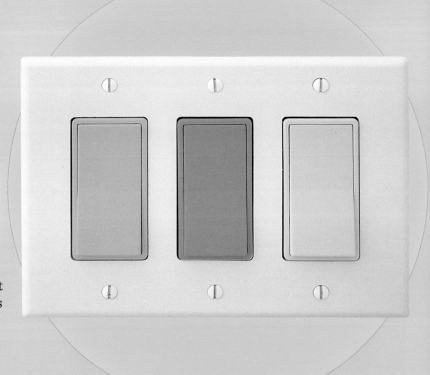

Answers on page 218

TRY IT!

DNA Recipe

Let's experiment with fruit to see how DNA works!

Why It Matters

Have you ever wondered what makes you unique? Unless you have a twin, there is no one else in the world who looks exactly like you, and it all boils down to DNA. It consists of four base chemicals that pair up. When a base is combined with a sugar molecule and phosphate molecule, you have a nucleotide that forms a double helix, often resembling a ladder. Packed into the nuclei of cells in strands called chromosomes, pure DNA is seen and handled by few except scientists, but here's your chance to learn more.

What You'll Need

Ripe strawberries

Ziploc bag

Liquid soap

Table salt

Coffee filter

Glass cup

Rubbing alcohol

Chopsticks

Strawberry DNA

1. Seal some ripe strawberries in a Ziploc bag, and gently squeeze them into mush.

2. Mix some liquid soap with a small scoop of table salt. Add the solution to the bag. Reseal, and gently squish again to dissolve the cell membranes.

3. Place a coffee filter over a glass cup. Pour the mixture through the filter to remove any solids. Now you have a DNA-rich cup of strawberry soap.

4. Tip the cup to one side and gently pour rubbing alcohol down the side of the cup. The alcohol should form a layer on top of the strawberry soap.

5. A white, stringy layer of DNA molecules will form between the alcohol and the strawberry soap. Use a chopstick to grab the DNA and slowly pull it out. It should emerge in long, gooey strands of intertwined macromolecules. These can be preserved in rubbing alcohol.

Did You Know?

LEDs can individually be set to emit a different color or be tuned to a specific color temperature. In the Sistine Chapel, engineers used 3000 Kelvin, a relatively warm temperature chosen because analysis suggests it's the best way to make the colors look as brilliant to us as they did to Michelangelo 500 years ago.

TRY IT!
LED Art

Art isn't confined to just colors anymore. Make it pop with lights!

Why It Matters

Michelangelo's masterpiece on the ceiling of the Sistine Chapel in Rome, Italy, has inspired countless generations of artists. Now it's been tech-ified with LEDs! With more than 7,000 new LEDs, the project presented the painting in a new light. Improvement like this is an important part of the maker mindset.

Pull an old art project out for display and learn more about using the science of circuitry by adding copper tape, a battery, and LEDs to your artwork.

1. Think About Placement. Will you put an LED right inside the art and make it a part of the art, such as a nose, eyes, lightning bugs, a horizon, or stars? Will they be the same or different colors? Perhaps, if you decide to frame your artwork with LEDs, you will choose a standard color so as to not take away from the art itself. The design is up to you!

2. Create Closed Circuits. Once you decide where you wish to place the LEDs, you have to get them to light up. Don't worry. They don't emit harmful UV rays or heat. So what's the best way to create those circuits?

a. Adhere your art to a solid backing like cardboard.

b. Run copper tape along the back. You will need to cut the tape, peel off the backing, and adhere it to the back of the cardboard.

c. Set a coin-cell battery on top of the copper strip so the negative side of the battery is touching the tape.

d. Attach more copper tape on the opposite side of the battery to adhere to the top. You do not want the tape to touch the negative side of the battery.

3. Troubleshoot. Make sure both sides of the battery are touching an end of the conductive copper tape that is touching the battery and that the negative and positive ends aren't touching each other,

especially if it doesn't initially light. Troubleshooting is the work of a maker and innovator!

4. Attach It to Your Art. Cut a hole where you want the LED to be placed and make sure the copper tape can secure the prongs on each side of the LED bulb. The longer prong is the positive side and the shorter prong holds the negative side.

5. Tape It Properly. Run copper tape out each side of the LED. Make sure the tape covers each part of the prong on each side. Connect the longer, positive copper tape to the tape leading to the positive side of the battery. Connect the shorter, negative LED side to copper tape leading to the negative side of the battery. It should light!

MAKE IT!
Squishy Circuits

Squishy circuits teach the basics of conductivity, cooking, and clay modeling. Plus, you can use them to make scary skeleton cookies!

Why It Matters

There's no doubt that working with playdough is fun—it can be molded into many unique creations. It can also be electrifying! With a little science, you can make playdough light up. Most playdough is conductive, which means it can carry electricity. Let's make some Halloween cookies that can light up with LEDs by creating closed circuits!

What You'll Need

3 cups white flour

¼ cup iodized salt

3 tablespoons cream of tartar

4 tablespoons vegetable oil

Food coloring

1 cup tap water

½ cup sugar

½ cup distilled water

Dry and liquid measuring cups and spoons

3-quart saucepan

Two sturdy spatulas

Waxed paper

1 medium ceramic or stainless-steel mixing bowl

One 9-volt battery

Two wire leads with alligator clips on each end

3- to 5-watt component LED bulbs in a variety of colors

Sculpt Your Squishy Circuit Masterpiece

We made a skull with red LED eyes for Halloween. It consisted of two layers. The top one—the mask—was insulating dough. Because this was made with sugar and distilled water, both of which lack the ions that conduct electricity, the dough had an insulating effect. We placed the mask over two conductive dough strips separated by an insulating one. Conductive dough contains table salt and tap water, which form an ion-rich electrolyte; electricity passes, or is conducted, from ion to ion.

The insulating strip lies laterally beneath the eyes. The conductive strips were close together, so you could stick the long and short legs of the LED into the positively and negatively charged dough, respectively, to complete the electrical circuit and light up the LEDs.

Create the Conductive Dough

1. Combine the dry ingredients in the saucepan: 1 cup flour, ¼ cup salt, and 3 tablespoons cream of tartar. Add 1 tablespoon vegetable oil, food coloring of choice, and 1 cup tap water and stir with a spatula.

2. Place the pan over low to medium heat and stir until the mixture is lumpy. Keep stirring, incorporating all of the ingredients, scraping the bottom of the pan so that they don't stick to it.

3. After the mixture forms a ball, set it aside to cool on waxed paper dusted with flour.

4. Gradually add about ½ cup flour, kneading the dough until it is the consistency of playdough.

Make the Insulating Dough

1. Combine 1 cup flour, ½ cup sugar, and 3 tablespoons vegetable oil in a medium bowl and stir with a spatula.

2. Add food coloring of choice to ½ cup distilled water.

3. Stir 1 tablespoon of the liquid at a time into the flour-sugar mixture and combine. Gradually, alternate adding the remaining water and kneading in about ¼ cup flour until the texture is like playdough.

Create the Circuit and Add Power and Lights

1. Roll two pieces of conductive dough and one piece of insulating dough into short cylinders, like little hot dogs. Smash together the three pieces, with the insulating dough in the middle. Make sure that the pieces of conductive dough are not touching each other.

2. Clip one end of each electrical lead to the positive and negative battery terminals, and connect the other ends to the pieces of conductive dough.

3. Insert the shorter of the two prongs of an LED into the conductive dough attached to the negative terminal, and the longer prong into the positively charged dough. You have just completed the circuit and the light should be glowing!

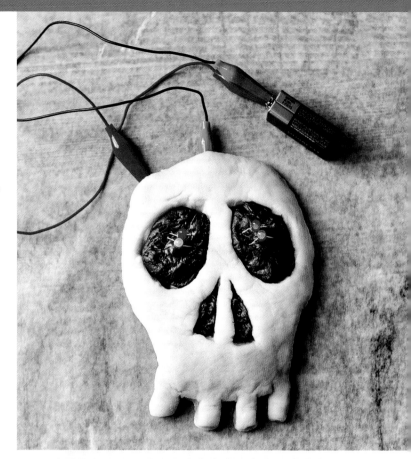

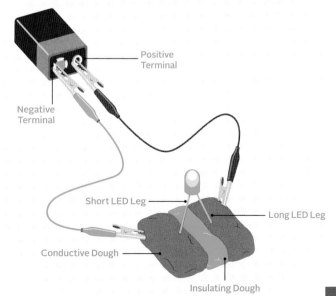

Positive Terminal

Negative Terminal

Short LED Leg

Long LED Leg

Conductive Dough

Insulating Dough

Take It One Step Further

Display your artwork in a dark room! If you prefer to use fluorescent paints, you will need a black light to watch the animals glow. Try experimenting with neon glitter. It really pops! What kind of story will your bioluminescent animal tell? Try writing a story to go along with your artwork.

TIP

Remember to "charge" your paint in the sun to activate the chemicals so your artwork will glow at night. If you don't want your artwork to fade from the sun over time, artificial lighting works well too.

3D Bioluminescence Art

Here's another activity inspired by deep-sea camouflage!

Why It Matters

Humans generate electricity, but not from their own bodies. Some animals can. These sea creatures are considered to be bioluminescent. How do they do it? The answer can be found in understanding the science of bioluminescence. Let's learn more before creating our own glow-in-the-dark art to resemble bioluminescence!

What You'll Need

Glow-in-the-dark poster paint or playdough

Paintbrushes

Pipe cleaners

Empty shoebox

Black construction paper or black paint

Plastic googly eyes

Pom-poms

Craft glue

Did You Know?

The oceanic abyss is home to some of the most interesting creatures on Earth. Slowly, the amazing biological secrets of these deep sea fish, who live most of their lives in near total darkness, are slowly coming to light.

A study published in *Current Biology* reveals that ultra-black fish—including Poromitra crassiceps, Idiacanthus antrostomus, and Anoplogaster cornuta—have the ability to absorb nearly all of the light that touches their skin, thanks to a combination of what the researchers call super absorptive scattering particles.

Many researchers have tried to take photos of these fish, but soon learned what made it so difficult to do so. They were ultra-black. Think blacker than the darkest black you've ever seen. Highly reflective, mirrored surfaces might be helpful camouflage for sea animals who dwell near the surface, but for deep-sea creatures, a spark of bioluminescent lighting against a reflective surface—like fish scales—could be the difference between remaining safely hidden and being discovered by a hungry predator.

Let's use our art skills to "shed light" on these incredible sea creatures!

Consider What Type of Art You Wish to Make. Do you want to use the black construction paper to paint and glue on 3D pieces like pompoms and googly eyes, or make 3D art in a shoebox lined with black paper and covered in glow-in-the-dark paint instead?

Do Some Research Online. Decide on a bioluminescent animal to create. Will you make art based on fireflies, octopuses, jellyfish, or anglerfish?

Start with the Black Background. Get a nice base either with black construction paper or paint. Make sure it's dry before you work with it further.

Add Your Bioluminescent Animal. Paint an outline of your animal. If you choose to add 3D items, lay down small amounts of glue onto the design and then stick on the 3D elements.

Make it Glow! After they are dry, paint over them with glow-in-the-dark paint to make sure they glow.

Adult Supervision Required!

Pumpkin-Carving Like A Pro

Grab an adult to help you with these pumpkin-carving tips and techniques that will ensure you'll have the best and spookiest-looking jack-o'-lantern in the whole neighborhood.

Why It Matters

Although carving a jack-o'-lantern from a fresh pumpkin isn't difficult, there are ways to make the process go more smoothly and safely. There's an art and science to selecting the right type of pumpkin to make the carving easier. Size and ripeness matter too! Specially designed tools can make for incredible designs if you know which ones to use. That's what being a maker is all about! Study your choices in tools and materials before you get started. When you are finished, you also need to decide how it will light. How innovative will you be? What kind of power supply will you use? Have a spooktacular time!

Pick the Right Pumpkin. Pumpkins are often divided into two categories: pie pumpkins and carving pumpkins. Pie pumpkins are small and round and ideal for baking. Carving pumpkins are larger, but have thinner walls and fewer guts, making them easier to cut into and clean out.

Before purchasing the pumpkin, rap on it with your knuckle in several spots to ensure there aren't any soft spots which indicate rot. And remember, the very freshest pumpkins last the longest, so consider buying your carving pumpkin at a "pick-your-own" farm.

Use the Right Carving Tool. You can carve pumpkins with various kitchen knives, but to step up your game, consider using clay-sculpting tools, such as wire-end ribbon tools, stainless steel scalpels, or wood-carving gouges. Execute cuts with a serrated knife, keyhole saw, or compass saw. To create round holes in the pumpkin, try using a cordless drill and spade bit.

If you want to add speed and power to the project, get a pumpkin-carving rotary tool, which comes with lots of different attachments for cutting, engraving, and carving jack-o'-lanterns.

Start Carving. Use a pen or marker to draw a circle around the top of the pumpkin. Use a serrated knife or saw to cut along the line to create a removable lid. Lift off the lid and use a large metal spoon, or similar tool, to scrape out the interior guts.

Next, mark the remaining cutouts onto the pumpkin, including eyes, nose, mouth, and teeth. Make the cutouts with a small paring knife or narrow saw, such as a keyhole saw. If you're having difficulty holding the pumpkin steady as you cut into it, get a large bowl. Line it with a double-thick terry cloth towel, then set in the pumpkin. The bowl will secure the pumpkin and the towel will keep it from sliding around.

Let There Be Light.
To illuminate your jack-o'-lantern, place a tea light candle in a glass votive holder and set it in the bottom of the pumpkin. Use a long match or lighter to light the candle and replace the lid. Drill a small, ½-inch hole in the lid to act as a chimney to allow heat to escape.

If using candles, place the pumpkin outdoors and away from anything flammable. To illuminate indoor jack-o'-lanterns, use either battery-powered flameless candles or remote-controlled LED pumpkin lights.

A Rotten Ending. Your completed jack-o'-lantern will last longer if you dip it in an ice bath with a cup of bleach. Rub petroleum jelly on the edges of the cutouts to seal in moisture.

Don't get too attached to your Halloween handiwork. Ultimately, it'll rot away or become squirrel food.

COLOR IT!

TIP

Use this as inspiration for your jack-o'-lantern design (page 44) or get creative and play with shapes to make it look more silly or scary.

COLOR IT!

FUN FACT

Once a cheetah sets its sight on its next meal, they use their lightning-fast speed (0-60 mph in 3 seconds!)—and the element of surprise thanks to their camouflaged fur—to hunt.

Take It One Step Further

Level up your next Hide and Seek game with friends and only use camouflage. See if you can stay completely still and wear clothing or a costume to disguise yourself in your habitat!

FUN FACT

In 1929, the Italians became the first to mass-produce camouflage. The M1929 telo mimetico combined large flowing shades of chocolate-brown and a gray-tinted green.

TRY IT!
Camouflage

Learn all about camouflage and create an "I spy" activity that's sure to stump friends and family.

Why It Matters

If you play a lot of hide-and-seek you probably have already started running out of brilliant hiding spots. The more people you play with, the fewer chances of finding a spot no one's looked in before. In the open fields of the savannah to the wide expanse of snow in the Antarctic, many animals use camouflage to protect themselves against predators. See how it's done in the animal kingdom and use that knowledge to excel in the next round!

What You'll Need

Paper

Pencil

Coloring pens

Do Research. Go online and find an animal that can camouflage itself and study it. How big is it? Where does it live? Is it prey or predator?

Draw. Start by making an outline on white paper. Don't forget to include its habitat! Could you add a predator nearby? Or would it be stalking its prey?

Add in Color. Remember: The animal should blend in with its habitat, so choose colors that make it hard to find. Ensure your colors are accurate based on your previous research about how it camouflages itself in the real world.

Test Friends and Family. See if they can find it in your picture. How long did it take them to spot your animal?

Different Types of Camouflage

All-Natural Camo
Some animals have fur, skin, or scales already designed to blend in with their habitat, like polar bears' white fur with snow and ice, and desert rattlesnakes with sand and rocks.

Predatory Patterns
Other animals can blend into their hunting environments with the patterns on their bodies, like stripes on a tiger and spots on a cheetah.

Color-Changing Chromatophores
Creatures, like chameleons and octopuses, have chromatophores which are special skin cells containing sacs of various pigments that allow them to change color when they tighten the muscles around these cells.

TRY IT!
Map and Compass

Using a compass is an essential skill—no batteries required!

Why It Matters

Have you ever gone on a hike and gotten lost in the woods? With a compass, you can navigate a map, shoot bearings to find your location, and even participate in fun activities like geocaching, an orienteering-based scavenger hunt. But it all starts with a little bit of science and math. Know your cardinal directions—north, south, east, and west—and never lose your way again!

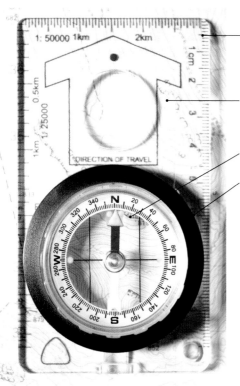

WHAT MAKES A COMPASS?

Baseplate: The plastic rectangle that makes up the base of your compass. The straight edges on the sides help to shoot bearings

Direction of travel arrow: The arrow fixed on the middle of the baseplate

Magnetic needle: This arrow, often red, is what points you north

Compass housing (bezel): The spinning marked with N, E, S, W, the cardinal directions, and 360 degrees, all of which help you head in the right direction

Orienting arrow: The arrow or box, usually about the width of the magnetic needle, drawn on the interior of the compass housing

Index line: The line that comes down from the direction of travel arrow and points to the bezel

SO, DOES THIS POINT NORTH?

Well, sort of. The magnetic needle on a compass points to magnetic north, rather than to the true North Pole. While the earth does act like a giant magnet with North and South Poles, the churning molten core makes magnetic north wander away from the pole.

In order to account for the difference between magnetic north and true north, every map will be marked with declination. This is the difference, in the specific area that that map covers, between true and magnetic north. This number varies depending on where you are in the world. If magnetic north lies directly between you and true north, then you'll have a declination of zero. But in most areas, you'll have to add or subtract to what your compass reads as north.

Because magnetic north is wandering, it's important to have a modern map. Even if the declination only changed by one degree, that can make an enormous difference over the course of a few miles.

SO WHERE DO I FIND THIS DECLINATION FIGURE?

Check the legend of your map, usually in one of the corners, which should also have the date the map was created so you can be sure you have an up-to-date map.

WHAT IF MY MAP IS OLD?

Worry not, head to the National Oceanic and Atmospheric Administration (NOAA) website to calculate your most up-to-date declination. If you own the map, go ahead and write the new figure down next to the old one, just make sure you date it.

HOW DO I FIND TRUE NORTH?

1. Hold your compass flat near your belly button, and let the magnetic needle settle. The red end points to magnetic north.

2. Spin the bezel of your compass until N (north) is in the center of the baseplate, with the index line pointing directly at N.

3. Rotate in place until the red arrow of your compass lies within the orienting arrow and points at N. You are now facing magnetic north.

4. Read your declination. If it reads X Degrees WEST, twist your bezel clockwise to subtract that number. If it reads X Degrees EAST, spin your dial counterclockwise to add that number on your bezel. If you have trouble remembering which way it goes, learn the rhyme in the next section.

5. Spin in place until the magnetic needle is once again inside of the orienting arrow. Now, the direction of travel arrow, and you are pointing true north.

HOW DO I ALIGN MY MAP WITH TRUE NORTH?

1. Lay your map on a flat surface. Beware of metal bolts on picnic tables which can affect the magnet.

2. With your compass pointing to true north, line the straight edge of the compass up with the north south lines of your map. Your map is now oriented toward true north.

3. Put rocks on the corners, or otherwise secure your map, so that it doesn't move while you navigate.

HOW DO I USE MY MAP WITH MY COMPASS?

1. With your map aligned to true north, look around you for two known landmarks. Mountains or lakes work well, and even water towers or road intersections can work great.

2. Find these landmarks on your map.

3. Pick up your compass, adjusted for true north, and point the direction of the travel arrow at your first landmark. Pick up your compass, adjusted for true north, and point the direction of the travel arrow at the landmark.

4. Spin the bezel of your compass until the needle is in the orienting arrow (put red Fred in the shed, as we used to say in Boy Scouts). The number at the index line is your bearing.

5. Put the compass on your map with one corner touching the landmark. With the compass corner touching the landmark, spin the compass until the needle is once again in the orienting arrow. Draw a line with a pencil on your map along the straightedge of your compass, intersecting your landmark.

6. Repeat steps 1-5 with your second landmark. Where the lines intersect is your location.

7. If you're on a trail, pay attention to how the land or trail around you corresponds to the map as you travel so you don't have to

continue shooting bearings. If you do get turned around, shoot bearings once again.

HOW DO I PICK THE RIGHT DIRECTION?

1. Align your map to true north.

2. With a straightedge, draw a line between where you are and where you want to be.

3. Put your compass straightedge, adjusted for declination, on that line, and turn the bezel until the needle is in the orienting arrow.

4. Pick up your compass, hold it flat, and put it against your belly button so the direction of travel arrow is pointing away from you. Turn yourself in place until the needle is in the orienting arrow. The direction of travel arrow now points where you want to go.

5. Pick a landmark in the distance that your direction of travel arrow points to, and walk to it. This makes it easy to stay true to your course.

Andromeda Galaxy

Deneb

Vega

Great Globular Cluster in Hercules

Arcturus

Pegasus

Altair

Saturn Mars

Eagle Nebula

Moon

Sagittarius

Butterfly Cluster

Milky Way

Take It One Step Further

After mapping out your favorite constellation, do some research on the internet. Discover what the name of the constellation represents (an animal, mythological persona, object, etc.). Can you draw the representation around the constellation to create the image with the constellation inside?

TIP

Watch out for shooting stars! Though not all constellations are visible at all times of the year from Earth, you never know what meteoroids are burning up as they enter the Earth's atmosphere.

TRY IT!
Constellation Mapping

Do you love stargazing? This astronomy activity is designed just for you! Pack a snack, a blanket, and binoculars, and head outside after nightfall to see what constellations you find.

Why It Matters

Have you ever tried to count what seems like an infinite amount of stars in the night sky? It's awe-inspiring, isn't it? But beyond being beautiful, the stars serve an important purpose. Did you know that sailors and astronauts use constellations—a group of stars that are arranged in a pattern—to navigate if their technology fails? Learn how by tapping into your science skills!

What You'll Need

Camping chair or blanket

Binoculars

Paper (or notebook)

Colored pencils

Flashlight

Ruler

Pencil

Compass

Prep In Advance. Look for a sky map or star finder chart online for the Northern Hemisphere if you live in the United States. Make note of what constellations are visible to you based on your location and the time of your observation.

Head Outside. Find a location that is dim or not well lit. For example, a country trail would be a much better option for a location than a well-lit city. A clear night with a moonless sky is best. Locate a spot where you can sit in a camping chair or lie down on a blanket without bending your neck too far.

Observe and Take Notes. Give your eyes some time to adjust to the lack of light. This may take about 20 minutes. Bring out a piece of paper (or a notebook) and colored pencils. With a flashlight on your paper, log the date, time, and location.

Draw. Using little circles to represent stars, plot out how a constellation of your choice appears in the night sky and fill them in completely. Can you name it without connecting the dots? If so, jot that down in your journal as well. Then use a ruler to draw straight lines in between stars and visualize the constellation in a different color.

Add Some Detail. If you have a compass, mark on your drawing where north points to on the needle. Draw the rest of your cardinal directions around it. If you have some landmarks from your location, like trees or buildings, sketching them around the perimeter of your drawing will help you notice changes over time.

Repeat. Do this for several nights in a row, preferably for a few weeks. What do you notice? Have the placements of your constellation changed over time? They should!

COLOR IT!

Meet Aglaonice

Connect the dots to reveal Aglaonice, widely considered the first female astronomer in ancient Greece, who focused her studies on the moon's cyclical patterns. Her lunar eclipse predictions were so accurate that many claimed she was a sorceress who had the power to hide the moon and make it reappear at her whim.

FUN FACT

African-American female pioneers Katherine Johnson, Dorothy Vaughan, and Mary Jackson were part of NASA's team of human "computers" who calculated complex equations by hand. This allowed space heroes like Neil Armstrong and Alan Shepard to travel to space and make it back safely.

Katherine Johnson

Dorothy Vaughan

Mary Jackson

SOLVE IT!
Rock-Paper-Scissors Riddle

Jack and Jill went up the hill and played a game of rock-paper-scissors. Who won?

Why It Matters

If you know the rules of the game, you're probably thinking it's all about luck. But the more you play, the more you learn about patterns and probability. What's the likelihood of your opponent using the same choice, let's say paper, more than twice in a two-minute span? If you're quick enough to calculate how many times your partner uses each choice, do you think that can give you an advantage? Here's a simple problem to see how quickly you can determine who wins the game.

Problem

Jack and Jill play rock-paper-scissors 10 times. You know that:

1. Jack uses rock three times, scissors six times, and paper once.

2. Jill uses rock twice, scissors four times, and paper four times.

3. There are no ties in all 10 games.

4. The order of the games is unknown.

Who wins?
By how much?

TIP
It can be tricky to figure out the solution just by looking at the list of information—grab a pad and pen.

Answers on page 219

SOLVE IT!

The Locker Prank

Here's a prank that won't get you into too much trouble—we hope.

Why It Matters

It seems simple enough, opening and closing the locker doors. However, you need to know your factors in order to solve the puzzle. Sure, you may find it funny putting your principal in a tailspin trying to figure it out, but imagine how great it would feel to get caught and be able to say you sharpened your math skills trying to pull off the prank of the year!

Problem

There are 100 lockers that line the main hallway of Chelm High School. Every night, the school principal makes sure all the lockers are closed so that there will be an orderly start to the next day. One day, 100 mischievous students decide that they will play a prank.

The students all meet before school starts and line up. The first student then walks down the hallway and opens every locker. The next student follows by closing every other locker (starting at the second locker). Student 3 then goes to every third locker (starting with the third) and opens it if it's closed and closes it if it's open. Student 4 follows by opening every fourth locker if it's closed and closing it if it's open. This continues until Student 100 finally goes to the hundredth locker. When the principal arrives later in the morning, which lockers does she find open?

Answers on page 219

TRY IT!
The Perfect Field Goal

Ever wondered what it would be like to be a football kicker in the National Football League? Using math and science, now you can!

Why It Matters

When Alex Henery, formerly of the Philadelphia Eagles and the Detroit Lions, stepped onto the field to attempt a kick, he had no time to worry about mechanics. Once the ball was snapped, he had 1.25 seconds to send it on its way. Sure, practice makes perfect, but many factors will influence the outcome of the play—force, speed, angle, and trajectory, to name a few. Let's dig deeper to learn how you, too, can make that field goal count!

1. The Hold. Everyone knows the laces should point away from the kicker's foot, but pros like Henery demanded that the ball be standing straight up, too. Tilting it lowers the center of mass, making it tougher to strike the sweet spot, says biomechanics professor Jeff Hawks, who studied Henery's technique with colleague Chase Pfeifer at the University of Nebraska, Lincoln.

2. The Plant. During his approach, Henery used to place his left foot, heel first, next to the ball—barely 10 inches from the nose. By positioning himself this close and pointing his planted big toe directly at the goalpost, the kicker opens his hips and draws power from the core muscles in his torso and legs.

3. The Arm. The 177-pound pro extended his left arm at a 90-degree angle, keeping his body in balance as his chest and hips face the target. While leg speed is crucial for distance, posture and

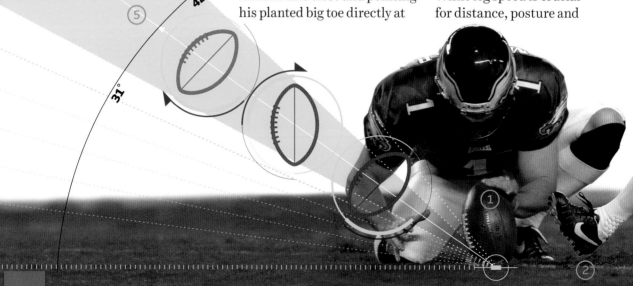

balance dictate accuracy, says Sacramento State professor of kinesiology David Mandeville.

4. The Kick. Any misplaced movement reduces velocity and energy. Henery struck the sweet spot with the top of his foot ("right where you tie your shoes," he says) and powered straight on through it. When he made contact with the ball, his foot was traveling 53 to 60 mph. By accelerating through the ball, he squeezed every bit of power from his upright kicking motion. The sweeping follow-through lets his foot reach peak speed in the 0.03 seconds after contact.

5. The Flight of the Ball. As a sophomore at the University of Nebraska, Henery once kicked a 57-yard field goal. He made it look so easy—and that's the whole point. When kickers break form, they get into trouble. With a perfect strike and no wasted energy, Henery could launch the ball at a velocity of 53 mph and 1400 rpm. The faster the rotation, the less drag the ball will encounter. If he tried to put more leg into the kick, odds are good he'd send the ball off on the wrong trajectory. According to Rodney Imamura, who researched kicks alongside David Mandeville and Michael Nava at Sacramento State, field goal attempts generally soar at an angle between 27 and 42 degrees. Henery's kicks were more precise, leaving his foot in the safe range between 31 and 41 degrees.

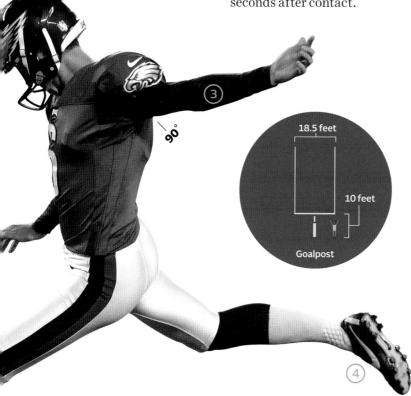

18.5 feet

10 feet

Goalpost

The Perfect Knuckleball

Pitching a knuckleball is much harder than it looks, but learning the math and science involved will have you striking your opponents out in no time!

Why It Matters

R.A. Dickey, formerly of the Toronto Blue Jays, Atlanta Braves, and several other Major League Baseball teams, is the first knuckleball pitcher to win the Cy Young Award. He can throw multiple knuckles using the same grip and motion—but have each one break differently. While science still has a hard time explaining why knuckleballs do the things they do, we can definitely explore the physics of the pitch and Dickey's mechanics of throwing it so you can try it the next time you step up to the plate.

---

1. Grip. Dickey dug into the leather with the nails of his index and middle fingers just behind the runway, where the ball's seams are closest together; he placed his thumb and ring finger on the sides of the ball. He kept his nails even with a fine-tooth glass file and strong with the nail-hardening product Trind. Nails are a vital stabilizing force that enabled

Dickey to release the ball with almost no spin.

2. Windup. Dickey loaded up energy by shifting his weight to his rear (right) foot, kicking up his left knee, and turning his torso clockwise. This motion is more deliberate and controlled than that of a "normal" pitcher.

3. Stride. Normal pitchers aim to generate maximum power by pushing hard off their back leg and hurtling laterally toward home plate. Dickey limited his leg push and kept his body upright, turning until his shoulders were square to the plate. His step forward was short. "Economy and

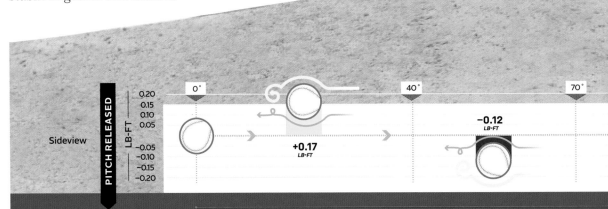

simplicity are what you're after with the knuckleball," he said.

4. Release. As Dickey moved his arm forward in front of his body, he loosened his grip and let the ball float off his fingertips with minimal rotational force. His knuckler could reach 84 mph, spinning 180 degrees or less as it traveled 60.5 feet.

THE LAUNCH

120°   140°   160°   180°

−0.10 LB-FT

+0.07 LB-FT

−0.12 LB-FT

+0.09 LB-FT

PITCH CAUGHT

60.5 FEET, 0.5 SECONDS

Chromatography in Leaves

Sometimes Mother Nature is odd. But one thing is for certain—it's always beautiful!

Why It Matters

There's a reason that tree leaves look green during the spring and summer: A green chemical called chlorophyll is inside them. Chlorophyll helps trees and other plants grow by converting light into the sugars they consume as food. During the fall, when the days are shorter, there is less light. That means chlorophyll has less to do, and it starts breaking down. Once the chlorophyll is gone, other minor colors—the oranges, yellows, reds, and purples you see in the fall—can show through. The brightness of those colors is determined by many things, such as heavy rainfall, low (but not freezing) temperatures, and cloudy skies. Scientists may not know for sure why this happens, but we can use the art and science of chromatography to learn more—and capture its magic and beauty.

What You'll Need

Different colored leaves in varying stages of maturity

Small glasses, one for each color category of leaves

Paper towel strips, slightly longer than the height of glasses you'll be using

Tablespoons, one for each small glass

Rubbing alcohol

Masking tape

1. Gather different colored leaves in different stages of maturity, preferably from the same tree. Then separate them based on the color group—green, red, orange, yellow, and brown are good categories. You will need close to ten leaves in each grouping.

2. Crush or crinkle the leaves and place them in the small glasses, separated by color category.

3. Place 3 to 4 paper towel strips in front of each color grouping.

4. Pour a tablespoon of clean rubbing alcohol into each glass and stir. Make sure to use a different spoon for each glass. Did you notice a change in color immediately? Let it sit for about 30 minutes in a cool, dark place (like a basement) where there is no exposure to sunlight.

5. Remove any remaining leaf particles and stir each mixture with the same spoon used previously. Let it sit in a dark place overnight.

6. Stir again the next day. Then, spoon a few drops of each solution onto a few paper towel strips.

TIP

Toilet paper will work, too, but paper towels have a thicker consistency that is woven to shorten travel time based on molecule size which better separates colors.

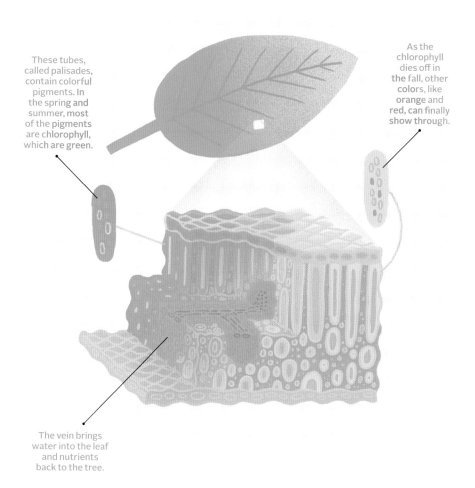

These tubes, called palisades, contain colorful pigments. In the spring and summer, most of the pigments are chlorophyll, which are green.

As the chlorophyll dies off in the fall, other colors, like orange and red, can finally show through.

The vein brings water into the leaf and nutrients back to the tree.

Take It One Step Further

To display your findings, you can gather more of the same leaves and do some art rubbings. Gently place paper over top of a leaf and, with some pressure, rub a crayon over it. You may need to draw the outer edges of the leaf, but the leaf's veins should be thick enough to show through. Have fun!

7. While the strips are drying, add another tablespoon of rubbing alcohol into the glasses and stir each one. Then, dip the paper towel strips into each liquid and note what you observe.

8. Secure the strips with masking tape around each glass. When colors reach the top after about a half hour, remove them and lay flat to dry. Make sure the strips don't touch each other while in the glass or after you take them out so as not to contaminate your results.

At this point, you should notice different bands of color on your test strips, based on the different pigments within the leaves. You will find orange carotenoids, yellow xanthophylls, and red anthocyanins. What observations can you make? Are all the separated colors on the same parts of the strips or in different places?

Take It One Step Further

Play around with items in different states of matter. Line up glasses with varying amounts of water and see how much ice you can add before it spills. What happens when you add ice to an already full glass? Does the amount change when the ice melts? Have fun experimenting!

TRY IT!

Icy Adventures

Everything is so much more beautiful in the winter—holiday decorations, snow-covered hills, and our favorite: sparkly icicles! Wondering how they form? Let's learn about the magic—and science—behind Mother Nature!

Why It Matters

Water freezes at 32 degrees Fahrenheit or 0 degrees Celsius. If you see layers of snow on your roof, then icicles will form soon. Science works here by combining sunshine to melt snow into water droplets that slowly spill off the ledge where below-freezing temperatures refreeze them. From knowing when to prepare for icy conditions, to figuring out how much ice to put in your lemonade, understanding how temperature changes different states of matter is important. The good news is that we don't need to wait for winter to explore different states of matter. Follow along and experience the wonders of changing matter!

What You'll Need

Water

Ice trays in various sizes and shapes

Freezer

A glass of lemonade (or your favorite drink, but it's optional)

Make Ice. Fill up an ice cube tray with water and place it in the freezer. Record the time and the temperature gauge in your freezer. Check on it every half hour. How long did it take the water to change its state of matter from liquid to solid ice?

Melt Ice. Once frozen, take the ice out of the freezer. Note the temperature on the thermostat in your house. Make sure the ice is not exposed to any other heating or cooling sources that could affect the trial. For example, don't place the ice container near a window where it is exposed to direct sunlight that could cause the ice to melt faster. Don't leave it on the floor where a pet might stop by and try to drink it either! How long did it take for the ice to melt?

Change It Up. Use ice trays that make unique shapes—ones that look like fruit or candy are fun to work with! You can also use a bowl or even adhere a base to cookie cutters (so water doesn't leak out). Does the amount of water affect how long it takes to freeze or melt?

Record and Repeat. Jot down your findings in a journal. Run through the experiment multiple times, altering the temperature in your freezer and your home to make it warmer or cooler. What did you notice?

SOLVE IT!
Mathematical Life Skills

Simple equations make your life better in many ways!

Why It Matters

If it hasn't already, math will soon creep into your everyday life. It helps you determine the ingredients for doubling a batch of brownies and how many pies to order for your pizza party. Here are some exercises that will come in handy.

Leaving a Tip

Calculating a tip is daunting, even for adults! The difference between pretax and taxed amounts on the bill can be confusing, but instead of moving a decimal point or adding anything, just multiply the total by at least 1.2 (current standard of 20 percent minimum), and leave at least that much.

Let's try it: Your bill for a whole pie with garlic knots and a soda comes to $21.22. To give a 20 percent tip, how much will you need to leave?

Baking Cookies

Cooking is a field of mathematics. It's easy to deal with one-to-one substitutions, like chocolate chips for raisins or gluten-free flour for wheat flour. What if your favorite recipe requires three eggs, but you only have two? You'll need to multiply everything in the recipe by the same fraction as the ingredient you have the least of. In this case: 2 out of 3 = ⅔.

If the recipe calls for the amounts below, how much do you need now that you only have two eggs?

   1   cup flour
   ¾   cup sugar
   ½   cup butter
   1½   cups chocolate chips
   1   teaspoon pure vanilla
        extract

Splitting an Uber

Apps exist to make splitting checks and sharing bills easy, but what if your phone suddenly runs out of battery? If you know the per-ride base rate and the cost per mile, just multiply the cost per mile by the distance, add the base cost and the tip, then divide by the number of people in your group.

Let's say: You and three other friends are taking a cab to visit a friend's house. You know that the base rate of a cab is $2.60, and it costs $2.70 per mile. From where you plan to take the cab, it's about a 4.5 mile ride without traffic. With a 20 percent tip, how much will each person have to chip in at the end of the ride?

Ordering Pizza

Deciding which pizza to order is daunting enough—pepperoni versus mushroom—but simple math can help you decide what size is the best value by area. Large sizes cost more , but they're usually cheaper by the inch than the smaller pizzas. But diameter isn't the only concern, because a smaller pizza is also disproportionately high in the area of crust.

If your local restaurant adds, say, an inch of crust around the outside, take each pizza size and subtract two to control for crust, then divide the cost by what's left.

So which is the better deal: a 10-inch pizza for $10 or a 15-inch pizza for $15?

Answers on page 220

The Best Way to Cut a Sandwich

Triangles vs. rectangles: Which way is best?

Why It Matters

What is the best way to cut a sandwich in half? Do you cut it so it's easy to hold without the contents spilling out? Or do you cut it so it looks attractive when you have friends over? Surely triangles don't really have "more sandwich," right? That's geometry and the law of conservation of matter. But something about the statement just feels right. Why is that? Let's do some math to figure it out!

How Many Bites is a Sandwich?

This is hard to pin down—some say it takes four bites, others say it's 16. Here's a rough guideline all mapped out. We used a weighted calculation here: The best bite is worth three, the okay bite is worth two, and the double-crust corner bite is worth one.

Rectangle

In a rectangular sandwich half, there's one perfect middle bite. It's surrounded by three okay bites that have one side of crust, then two corner bites that have double-crust edges. Let's calculate for the average bite using the weighted calculations:

(3 + (3 x 2) + 2 x 1)) / 6 = 1.83 average bite

Triangle

The triangle shape naturally encourages bigger bites. It has one great middle bite, two okay side bites, then one bad bite with double crust. Let's calculate:

(3 + (2 x 2) + (1 x 1)) / 4 = 2.00 average bite

Rectangle vs. Triangle: The Verdict

While the math above and a quick survey showed that a triangle cut is a clear winner, people did bring up a few interesting points in the survey:

> **Triangles are right for BLTs.**
>
> **Rectangles are right for egg or tuna salads.**
>
> **Triangles make for better food styling.**
>
> **Rectangles are best for structural integrity.**

Plot Twist: A Third Option!

From that same survey, people have also suggested cutting sandwiches into trapezoids.

How does it perform in our math test? Most likely, people bite off the narrow end first, which is a bad corner bite; then there's one great middle bite and two okay bites divided by the diagonal.

(3 + (2 x 2) + (1 x 1) / 4 = 2.00 average bite

So, it's the same average as the triangle! Definitely worth a try!

Maybe it's easier to eat with rectangles, or triangles make it easier to finish lunch quicker. In the end, it's still all about preference, but according to math, triangles offer the best return on your sandwich investment.

MAKE IT!

Adult Supervision Required!

Detergent Bottle Ukulele

It's the perfect first instrument for any kid. Time to rock out!

Why It Matters

Let's engineer a ukulele with some building skills and science. You will need to tune the strings to affect the pitch. This is achieved through the adjustment of the tension of the strings. Also, the soundboard will amplify the vibration of the strings to enhance the sound. A heavier pound fishing line will produce a different sound than a lighter pound weight. Pretty cool, right?

What You'll Need

1 sheet each of medium and fine sandpaper

24-inch length of 1⅝- x ⅝-inch solid pinewood or similar lumber, such as ash

Handsaw or jigsaw

Ruler and pencil

50-ounce laundry detergent bottle, emptied, cleaned, and capless

Utility knife

Wood glue

⅜-inch-square hardwood dowel, at least 4 inches long

¼-inch-square hardwood dowel, at least 8 inches long

Small C- or spring clamp that opens at least 1 inch wide

Drill and 1⁄16-inch bit

8 small screw eyes

2 lengths of fishing line (40-inch lengths of 40-pound); 1 40-inch piece each of 50- and 60-pound fishing line

Fasten the Neck to the Bottle

1. Sand the pine until the sides are smooth.

2. Measuring from one end of the pine piece (the neck), mark pencil lines at 4¾, 15⁹⁄₁₆, 16³⁄₁₆, 16⅞, 17⁹⁄₁₆, and 18⅜ inches.

3. Trace the outline of one end of the neck on the bottom of the bottle. Use a utility knife to cut along the outline, creating an opening that's as flush as possible with the front of the bottle.

4. Mark the neck's exit point approximately 5 to 6 inches from the bottom opening. Trace the outline of the end of the neck on the bottle and cut out the exit hole.

5. Slide the neck into the bottom hole and out through the top of the bottle until ³⁄₁₂ inches of wood is sticking out from the bottom. Trace a line on the neck marking the bottom of the bottle.

6. Mark pencil lines on the bottle 4¼ and 4¾ inches from the bottom end of the neck. Place the ruler along the top edge of the neck where it enters the bottom of the bottle and draw a line connecting the two you just drew. Repeat at the bottom edge.

7. Remove the neck from the bottle and use the utility knife to cut out the rectangle formed by the four pencil lines you just drew.

CONTINUED ON NEXT PAGE!

FUN FACT
Did you know the word "ukulele" translates to "jumping flea"?

Detergent Bottle Ukulele

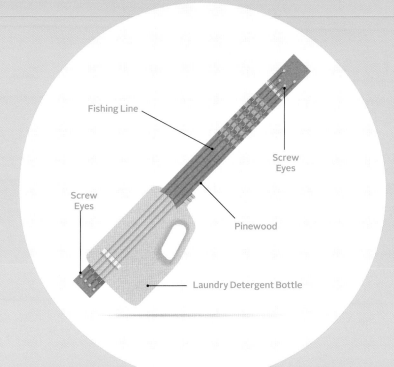

Fishing Line

Screw Eyes

Screw Eyes

Pinewood

Laundry Detergent Bottle

3. Mark a line 1¾ inches from the right end of the neck and drill pilot holes ¾ inch and 1½ inches from the top edge. Mark another line 3¼ inches from the right edge and drill pilot holes ⅜ inch and 1⅛ inches from the top edge. Fasten the four screw eyes into the wood.

4. Starting ⅜ inch apart from the top edge of the neck, mark four lines across the top nut. Using a utility knife, carefully incise ¹⁄₁₆-inch grooves along each of the lines.

5. To attach the strings, take 36 inches of the 40-pound fishing line and knot one end to the top left screw eye. Stretch the other end across the ukulele and slide it through the top right screw eye until there's about ¾ inch of slack in the line. Twist the screw eye clockwise.

6. Repeat the process, tying the 60-pound line to the next set of screw eyes, the 50-pound line to the third set, and the 40-pound line to the bottom set.

7. Use the notes G–C–E–A to get your ukulele in key by turning the screw eyes at the top of the neck. Download an MP3 tuner to ensure your every little note plucked is pitch-perfect.

8. Slide the bottle back onto the neck until the bottle's bottom is aligned with the mark you drew; the pencil line at 4¾ inches should be visible.

Glue the Dowels to the Neck

1. Cut two 1⅝-inch-long pieces of the ⅜-inch dowel.

2. Cut four 1⅝-inch-long pieces of the ¼-inch dowel.

3. Glue one ⅜-inch dowel piece onto the top surface of the neck through the bottle's rectangular cutout. Clamp until dry.

4. Glue a piece of ¼-inch dowel centered along each of the first four pencil marks (lengthwise down the center of the dowel). Clamp each piece until dry.

5. Glue down a ⅜-inch dowel piece with its short edge aligned to the 13⁹⁄₁₆-inch pencil line. Clamp until dry. This is your top nut.

Secure the Strings

1. Place the ukulele faceup on a table with the bottle handle at the bottom. Mark a line 1¼ inches from the left end of the neck. Drill a pilot hole into the line ¾ inch from the top edge, and then three more spaced ⅜ inch apart.

2. Tightly twist in four screw eyes.

TRY IT!
Gift-Wrapping Trick

Become a gift-wrapping pro in no time!

Why It Matters

It takes math and art skills to create a beautifully decorated and well-wrapped package. The secret to not wasting excess pieces is geometry.

What You'll Need

2 books
(4- x 5-inch or any rectangular item)

2 sheets of 7- x 9-inch wrapping paper

Here's how most people traditionally wrap a gift. This shows the leftover square we typically conceal with a separate piece you tape on as a patch.

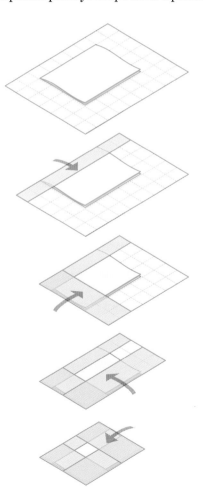

Now, how about turning the wrapping paper 45 degrees. Just by looking at how the "book" rests on the sheet, doesn't it already look like you have more wrapping paper to work with?

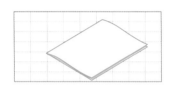

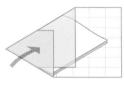

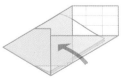

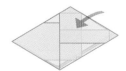

Take It One Step Further

Build an algorithm to give precise instructions, and test it out on a friend. Did they wrap the package efficiently? Fine-tune the algorithm and see if you can program a real robot to do it!

TRY IT!
Upcycled Art

Upcycling is taking old things and giving them new purpose. Let's uncover the most common recycling myths, and then create an art piece!

Why It Matters

Remember the old saying: One man's trash is another one's treasure? But there's more to recycling than just putting every plastic, cardboard, and glass item into the blue bin. Let's unclutter all the confusion—and then make fun art out of it!

Myth No. 1:
I can toss electronics in recycling.

Many people still assume that anything that seems recyclable—like items made of plastic, glass, and metals—must be. But in the case of electronics, that is not true at all.

Because of lithium ion batteries, smartphones that end up in trash heaps often explode and catch on fire. Yes, they can be recycled and reused, but they need to go to a specialty facility that knows how to handle these materials, commonly known as "e-waste."

Most common e-waste, like computers, tablets, and smartphones, can be taken to your local donation center, where devices can be repaired and resold, or taken to an electronics recycling center that can handle disassembly and recycling.

CONTINUED ON NEXT PAGE!

Myth No. 2:
Materials can only be recycled once.

This is false. You can look into the materials you're tossing and see how many times they can be recycled.

Plastic is one of the materials with a short recycling life, as plastic bottles don't become plastic bottles again—they're downgraded to plastic pellets that might then be recycled into rugs or clothing, which are, in turn, nonrecyclables.

However, metals like aluminum cans be recycled time and again without degradation. Glass is the same.

Myth No. 3:
Plastic bags are recyclable.

You are not supposed to put your plastic shopping bags into the recycling bin at home, which is why so many stores now offer cheap reusable bags near the checkout aisle.

Yes, most bags are made of recycled material, but recycling facilities don't want them, and it's partly due to single-stream recycling.

You dump all of your recyclables into one container, and those items are mixed together with all of those from your neighbors.

At a recycling facility, workers then separate plastic from glass from cardboard, etc., and the recyclables go into a machine that separates flat items from bottles and other containers.

Lightweight bottles and cans are separated from glass by air jets.

Aluminum cans are electrically charged and repel into their own bin as magnets pull out other metals.

Infrared light can detect up to seven different types of plastic. In the end, you get bales of compacted, recycled waste.

Upcycled Art

Here's how it works:
Plastic bags can get problematic.

a. When you toss them into the recycling bin, they get wet and dirty from other items, and there's not enough staff to clean and dry them, making the bags too nasty to resell.

b. There also is no mechanical process for separating plastic bags from other recyclables.

c. Worst of all, they get tangled up in the sorting equipment, sometimes accidentally ending up in the bales of separated paper. If just one half percent of a bale is contaminated with other materials, it can't be sold to reuse companies.

Instead, drop your plastic shopping bags at a special facility, like a plastic bags-specific recycling bin at school.

Keep in mind that when we say "plastic bags" here, we mean plastic shopping bags (the kind you get your groceries in, for example). Other types of plastic bags—like one gallon freezer bags or sandwich bags—can be recycled. Just be sure to snip the zipper portion off the bag first. This portion cannot be processed.

Myth No. 4:
Recycling Uses More Energy Than Making Something New.

According to the United States Environmental Protection Agency, recycling aluminum cans can save 95 percent of the energy needed to make new ones from raw materials and recycling steel or tin cans can save 60 to 74 percent of that energy. Paper saves about 60 percent, and the energy saved from recycling one glass bottle can operate a 100-watt light bulb for four hours.

Myth No. 5:
Recycling Pays for Itself.

We wish this were true, but it's not.

Plastic and glass are pretty cheap upon first use but, as mentioned earlier, there are sorting challenges for these two materials that drive up costs.

Although there are entrepreneurs looking at new business models to make recycling more profitable, we're not there yet.

Myth No. 6:
Separating Trash From Recyclables Isn't Important.

According to the United States Environment Protection Agency, "putting items in the recycling bin that can't be recycled can contaminate the recycling stream. After these nonrecyclable items arrive at recycling centers, they can cause costly damage to the equipment."

Similar to plastic bags that get tangled up in the machinery used in recycling facilities, common trash items can also clog the equipment.

Myth No. 7:
What You Recycle Must Be in Good Condition.

Imperfect items can still head to the recycling facility, as much of it will be melted or compressed into pellets anyway.

There is one exception: Broken glass can be dangerous for those who collect your recyclables, so be sure to place any shards of glass in a cardboard box first, or make sure it's wrapped in newspaper before placing it in the bin. Some facilities will take pieces of glass or broken bottles if the glass pieces are three inches or larger, so check with your local facility.

Now, let's see how well you can recycle. Determine if the statements below are true or false.

1. Sandwich bags can be recycled.

2. A crunched up can of soda cannot be recycled.

3. Your old tablet cannot be recycled.

4. It's fine to throw your plastic shopping bags into your recycling bin at home.

5. Recycling aluminum cans can save 60 to 74 percent of energy needed to make new ones from raw materials.

Answers on page 220

Let's Get Creative!

Now that you know what should and should not be recycled, let's make some art following all the steps of the engineering design process!

1. Define Your Problem. This process can go one of two ways: You create art based on a design you already have in mind, or you make art based on the materials you already have on hand. What do you want to make?

2. Brainstorm Ideas for Your Build. You may find inspiring ideas online that might help you with your design. Some questions to ask yourself:

> **a.** What materials will I use? Should I rely on items I already have a stockpile of, or will I need to go on a hunt for them?
>
> **b.** How will I fuse them together?
>
> **c.** Will I stick to one medium?
>
> **d.** How will I make it look appealing?
>
> **e.** Will I need to cut materials apart or can I get away with keeping them whole?
>
> **f.** Should I reuse an idea from a previous project and make a 3D model of it using recycling materials?

3. Pick the Best Solution. You can also gather feedback from family and friends and make sure you evaluate why your design will work. Don't forget to factor in the weather!

TIP

Some ideas of materials you can use include water bottles, newspapers, cereal boxes, egg cartons, lids, and paper towel rolls. Don't forget that e-waste is also an option!

4. Build Your Prototype. Get creative!

5. Test and Improve Your Design. Step away to reflect on it and think about what could make your design better.

6. Share It with the World. Take a picture and post it online. Or hold your own art exhibition. Maybe even design a larger-than-life piece to commemorate a playground or park in your neighborhood.

Take It One Step Further

Tell your story. They say that beauty is in the eye of the beholder. In most cases, people connect more deeply with art when taken in context. What inspired the art? What statement are you trying to make? Write a short paragraph about why you chose to make this art and include it as a caption when you share it with the world!

The Absolute Best Way to Eat an Oreo® According to Science

Calling all twisters, lickers, and dunkers: This activity is for you!

Why It Matters

Using science, you can trigger your brain to have a more enjoyable experience when eating an Oreo. Does the smell of chocolate change your experience when blended with the taste of vanilla? Do you find the circular shape easier to handle as a sandwich or split it up? Do you like licking the vanilla off, or do you find satisfaction in the crunch of biting into it? Try it warm and mixed in with a fresh stack of pancakes or finely chopped and cooled in ice cream. Put all your five senses to work to decode the experience.

Taste It. Oreo's cookie and creme make for a dynamic duo—the chocolate's rich, warm, slightly earthy smell fits well with sweet tastes, like vanilla. And while this treat is sweet, it also packs a certain amount of fat. As food scientists know, sugar and fat make a winning combo if you're aiming to supercharge your brain's reward system. Try it with one bite, or lick off the creme first.

Smell It. Oreos don't mesmerize with taste alone; aromas have a huge impact on the eating experience as well. When you bite into an Oreo, chemicals in the cookie release odorants into the air inside your mouth, says Linda Flammer, a senior research associate at Philadelphia's Monell Chemical Senses Center. These aromas flow to your nasal cavity, where they interact with smell receptors and enter your brain's decoding process.

Listen To It. Humans like noisy foods. "When we bite into something that makes noise, the sound draws our attention to our mouth so we're more aware of what we're tasting," says Charles Spence, a professor of experimental psychology at the United Kingdom's University of Oxford. The soft snap of an Oreo's dark cocoa-rich wafer could tell your brain that the cookies are "freshly baked."

Look At It. We perceive round foods as more approachable than jagged and angular foods, and we associate roundness with sweetness (think: a scoop of ice cream or the round base of a cupcake or a muffin). On top of their welcoming shape, Oreos are uniform, which creates familiarity, says Curtis Luckett, director of the University of Tennessee's Center for Sensory Science.

Feel It. Depending on how you eat it, texture plays a big role in your experience. Snack foods can be creamy, crunchy, wavy, puffy, crispy, smooth, gummy, chewy, soft-baked, and flaky; combinations and contrasts between these textures appear in popular foods across many different cultures. When it comes to Oreos, Luckett says, "you have texture attributes that are generally well-liked: You've got the smooth and creamy and the crispy and crunchy."

So What Is the Best Way to Eat an Oreo?

While the best-known way to eat an Oreo is the classic "twist, lick, and dunk," there are so many other ways to enjoy this sweet treat. After using all your five senses, it all comes down to personal preference. You can intensify your Oreo enjoyment by identifying your own texture preferences. Part of the Oreo's popularity can be traced to its manipulability: All types of eaters can optimize the treat to their desires.

Now, what is your absolute favorite way to eat an Oreo?

Four Categories of Eaters

Members of the Understanding and Insight Group, a product and strategy development firm, used research to divide people into "mouth behavior types":

Crunchers use "forceful mouth action" to make a fast and loud effect (think Bugs Bunny).

Chewers like the sensation of chewing so much that they "look for fullness in the mouth" and "turn the food into a moist mass."

Smooshers use their tongues and palates to mash their food.

Suckers literally try to suck flavor out of foods before chewing and swallowing. (Ever let chocolate melt on your tongue?)

MAKE IT!
Candy Dispenser

This is much more fun than a bowl on the counter!

Why It Matters

Who doesn't love candy? Toss it in the air and catch it in your mouth. Maybe slowly peel away at the wrapper and savor it melting on your tongue. Or you could jiggle small pieces out of the bag and into your hands. There are many ways to enjoy it. We especially like the excited anticipation that comes with using a candy dispenser. Precise measurements will be key to making this work efficiently.

What You'll Need

1 Dispenser box top (A) 1- x 1- x 6-inches

1 Back panel (B) ¼- x 8- x 10-inches

2 Dispenser box sides (C) 1- x 1- x 1-inch

1 Distribution rod (D) ¾- x 14-inches

6 Obstacle dowels (E) ⅜- x 2-inches

3 Obstacle blocks (F) 1- x 1- x 1-inch

2 Catch-box sides (G) 1- x 1- x 8-inches

2 Catch-box sides (H) 1- x 1- x 4-inches

1 Catch-box bottom (I) ¼- x

6- x 8-inches

1 Catch-box divider (J) scrap, 4-inch long

1 Clear plastic panel (K) ³⁄₁₆- x 8- x 10-inches

4 Pan-head screws (L) No. 8 ⅝-inch

2 Wood screws (M) 2-inch

1 Cork (N)

Jigsaw

Backsaw

Plastic miter box

Wood glue

1 Box brad nails 1-inch

Needle-nose pliers

Hammer

Drill

1. Mark the panel dimensions for the back of the dispenser box and the catcher on the sheet of plywood. Cut to size with a jigsaw and an 8-tpi wood-cutting blade.

2. Cut remaining wood parts to size using a backsaw and a plastic miter box.

3. Use a ¾-inch-diameter spade bit to make the two holes for the distribution rod in the sides

and one for the cork in the top block of the dispenser box. Align the three pieces to form the box and apply a bead of wood glue to the surface.

4. Press the back panel into position on the glued frame. Holding brad nails with needle-nose pliers to prevent pinched fingers, drive the brads through the plywood into the box sides and top. Repeat this process to form the catch box.

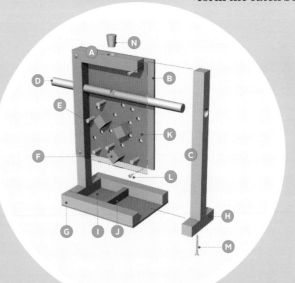

CONTINUED ON NEXT PAGE!

Project Notes

To sand the inside of the dowel holes, wrap sandpaper around the drill bit and run it briefly in each hole.

When you go to pre-drill the screw holes in the plastic sheet, make sure the bit is slightly larger than the screw shank. We cracked two sheets using too-small holes.

Finally, don't store the dispenser in the window. At least not when it's full. Jellybeans melted together, and M&M's softened so much they got crushed when we turned the dowel.

Candy Dispenser

5. Use a ⅜-inch twist drill bit to drill five to ten holes in the back panel of the distribution box. Glue the obstacle blocks to the panel. Anywhere is fine.

6. Position the precut plastic panel over the box frame, bore pilot holes for its mounting screws, and screw down the plastic cover. Insert dowels randomly in the holes in the back panel.

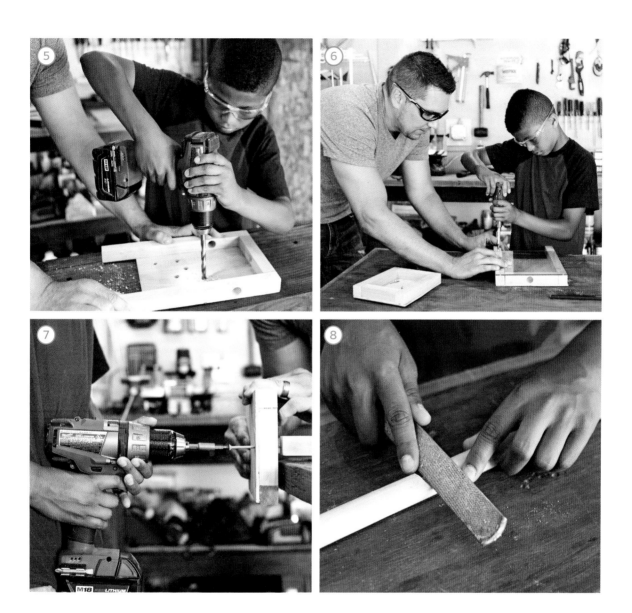

7. Hold the distribution box flat on the workbench, up against the edge. Butt the catch box up to it and drill a pilot hole through the bottom of the catch box and into the sides of the distribution box. Fasten with 2-inch wood screws.

8. Cut a notch for the candy to fall through into the pivoting dowel using the half-round surface of a wood rasp. Fit the dowel in the box and turn it to check for free movement. Add candy.

What You'll Need

1 pound fresh strawberries (rinsed and hulled; makes about 2 cups crushed)

4 cups granulated sugar

¾ cup water

1 box Sure-Jell pectin (yellow box)

6 glass jars with sealable lids (Mason jars with screw-on lids work best)

Saucepan

Oven mitts

2 large bowls

Measuring cups

Drying towel

Ladle

Knife

Masher

Food thermometer

How to Store

Jam you plan on eating in the next few weeks may be placed in the refrigerator. Consider freezing the rest until you are ready to thaw, but consume them within a year.

TRY IT!

Canning Strawberry Jam Preserves

Because homemade always tastes better than store-bought.

Why It Matters

Our ancestors had viable ways of preserving food before technology enabled inventions like the refrigerator and freezer. Now, we take them for granted, as they are considered a staple in most homes. Yet, there is something to be said for homemade goods that are preserved more naturally than processed foods. Learn to can and pickle for yourself using science and math.

1. Prep your materials. Make sure your saucepan, bowls, masher, knife, measuring cups, jars, and ladle have been thoroughly cleaned and sanitized, preferably in a dishwasher with exposure to boiling hot water to eliminate all germs.

2. Prepare your ingredients. After rinsing and hulling, dry strawberries using a towel before making jam. Be sure none of the stems or green leaves remain.

Note: Drying may take several hours. Strawberries are naturally made of water. You will want to avoid having excess water accumulate as part of your recipe, because it will change the consistency and taste later in the process.

3. In a large bowl, use a masher to beat the strawberries until a thick liquid mixture with pulp remains. Scoop out two cups of the mixture and transfer to another large bowl. Slowly, mix in sugar and let sit for about 10 minutes. This extra time allows the sugar to begin dissolving into the strawberry pulp mixture.

4. In a saucepan, add water. Pour in Sure-Jell. Stir quickly to prevent and minimize lumps.

TIP

Be sure to wash your hands and avoid touching the insides of the lids or jars to avoid any potential bacterial growth of mold. This also means sanitizing all surfaces.

Then turn on heat to high and bring your mixture to a boil. Stir constantly to keep mixture from hardening. Let boil for one minute until the temperature reaches 220 degrees, the setting point for jam.

5. Remove pectin mixture immediately from the heat source and pour it into the strawberry mixture, stirring vigorously for about three minutes to completely dissolve the sugar. Once dissolved, pour into canning jars, leaving about ½-inch unfilled at the top to allow for expansion once set. Seal jars tightly.

6. To set properly, let jars sit at room temperature for 24 hours before refrigerating or freezing—it will thicken to the right jam consistency.

MAKE IT!

Stilts

Stand tall—like a foot taller!

Why It Matters

The key to this project is a sturdy design that's fast and simple to build. Using math and engineering skills, you can design stilts to withstand your weight while making functional adjustments based on your height to maximize efficiency. See how different the world looks from a higher vantage point!

What You'll Need

3 studs (2- x 3-inches x 8-feet)

1 Box No. 10- x 3-inch construction screws

8 hex-head lag screws (¼- x 5-inches)

80-grit sandpaper

120-grit sandpaper

Miter saw or circular saw

Cordless drill

Square

⅛- x 6-inch drill bit

Sander

1. Crosscut two 2 x 3s to the dimensions shown in our cut list [A, B, C, D].

2. Determine how high up you want the bottom support block to be. (We recommend anywhere from 12 to 18 inches, depending on the height, enthusiasm, and agility of the stilt walker.) Then mark a reference line across the main stilt [A] and secure the bottom support block [D] below the line with two 3-inch construction screws.

3. Center the footrest [C] on the bottom support block so that there's equal overhang on both ends. Secure it with two 3-inch construction screws driven through the footrest and into the bottom support block [D].

4. Flip the stilt over and position the side support blocks [B] against it, centered on the footrest. Drive one 3-inch construction screw through the center of each support block and into the footrest.

5. Turn the stilt on its side and use a 6-inch-long, ⅛-inch-diameter drill bit to make a pair of pilot holes through the side support blocks [B] and into the body of the stilt [A]. Drive a ¼- x 5-inch lag screw into each pilot hole.

6. With a sander (or a square of sandpaper), use 80-grit followed by 120-grit to carefully sand the stilts where the user's hands will grip. If there are any sharp corners on the tops of the support blocks or footrests, reduce them with the 80-grit paper.

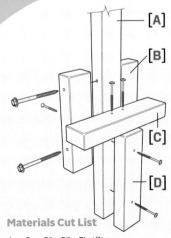

[A]

[B]

[C]

[D]

Materials Cut List

A	2	2" x 3" x 5' stilts
B	4	2" x 3" x 9" side supports
C	2	2" x 3" x 11" footrests
D	2	2" x 3" x 1' bottom supports

1

2

[A]

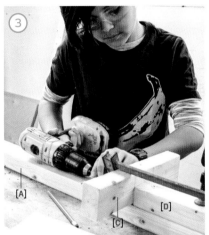

3

[A]
[C]
[D]

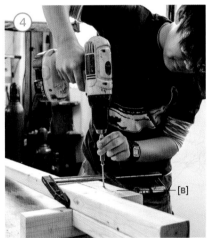

4

[B]

5

[A]
[B]

6

1 TIP

Don't forget to sand down where the stilt user puts his or her hands and where the body of the stilts rubs against the person's arms! While you're at it, knock off any sharp corners on the footrests or support blocks.

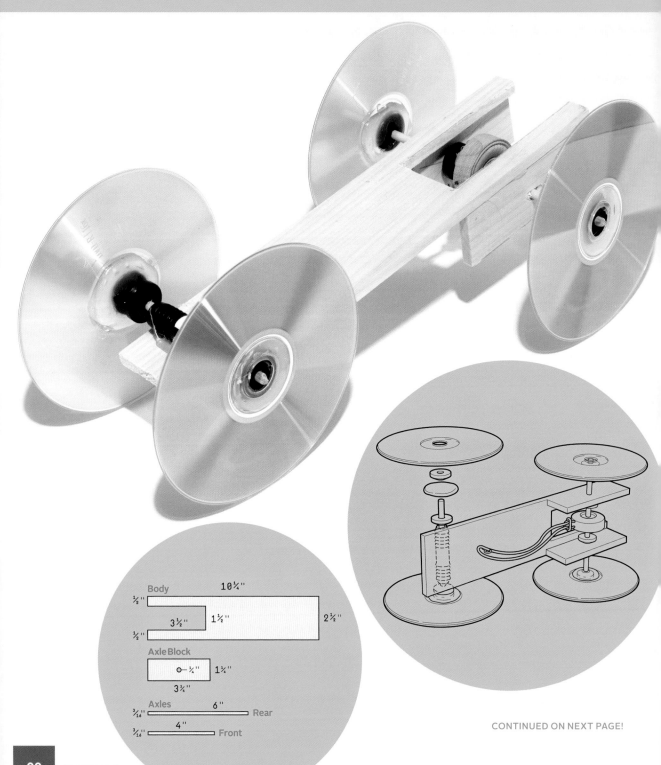

Body   10¾"

½"

3½"   1½"   2½"

½"

Axle Block

○—¼"   1¼"

3¾"

Axles

³⁄₁₆"   6"   Rear

³⁄₁₆"   4"   Front

CONTINUED ON NEXT PAGE!

Wind-Up Dragster

Did you know you can engineer a wind-up dragster using stored energy from a rubber band? Let's learn how to build a prototype!

Why It Matters

If you've ever played with a wind-up toy, you'll notice how it slows down and eventually stops after it uses up the stored energy from the initial wind-up. Maximize that energy by keeping it light. A heavy mass won't travel nearly as far. Reduce friction by making sure the axles are free to rotate and not rubbing against other parts. Aerodynamics come into play with air resistance, so the thrust and propulsion are key when releasing the stored energy from the rubber band. Follow along and see how far your dragster runs!

What You'll Need

¼- x 2½- x 24-inch poplar block

1 Package ½ L beveled washers

1½-inch-diameter birch tread wheel

1 Package (two pieces) ½-inch brass cup hooks

½-inch plastic barbed irrigation fitting

³⁄₁₆- x 48-inch poplar dowel

3 hot-glue sticks

10-inch rubber band

4 old CDs

1 jumbo paper clip

Drill

Jigsaw

Pliers

1. Mark the outline of the car body (see right) on the poplar block. Using a ⅜-inch bit, drill two holes at the interior corners of the U-shaped rear axle cutout. Use a jigsaw to make a parallel cut to each hole. Cut between the holes to form the U.

2. Rip and crosscut the two blocks that will support the rear axle. Make diagonal marks on one of the blocks to find the center, then clamp both to the workbench and bore a ¼-inch hole through the center mark.

3. Cut two dowel rods to length with cutting pliers. Clamp the birch wheel and drill two small holes in its side with a ³⁄₆₄-inch bit. Chop the end off a paper clip with pliers, then insert

the remaining U-shaped piece into the holes and secure with hot glue.

4. Twist the cup hook into the bottom of the car body, 2⅜ inches back from the front. On the opposite side, one inch back from the front edge, affix the irrigation tube to the body with hot glue.

5. Attach the rear axle blocks to the body with hot glue. Push the axle through one block, then slide on a beveled washer, the birch wheel, and another washer. Push the axle out through the opposite block, center the wheel, and affix it with hot glue.

6. Slide the front axle through the axle tube and add beveled washers to either side.

Wind-Up Dragster

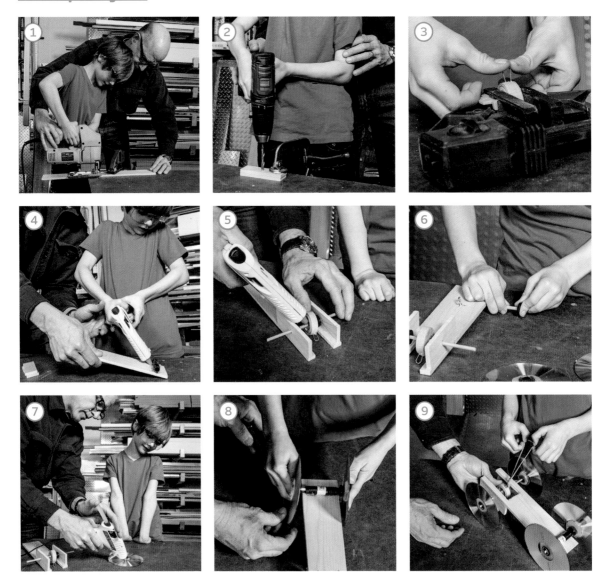

7. Affix the flat side of a beveled washer to each CD wheel with hot glue, then reinforce the seal by covering it with a dome of glue, being careful not to block the axle hole.

8. After the glue cools, press the wheels onto the axles.

9. Loop one end of the rubber band through the paper clip winder on the birch wheel and place the other over the cup hook. Rotate the wheels backwards to wind the rubber band, place the racer on the floor, and let it go.

Rolling Comeback Can

The physics involved in this project are complex, but the effect is simply cool: Roll the can away from you and watch as it stops and rolls back thanks to a rubber band and a weight.

Why It Matters

Ever thought about why a boomerang flies back to you after throwing it? Or have you wondered why some objects take longer to come back down after being catapulted into the sky? It's all in the science of physics. Gravity takes over and the weight of aerodynamic components (such as wings) can play a huge factor. In this activity, you'll learn about how gravity plays a part, as well as how transference of energy takes place to keep the can in motion. Let's get rolling!

What You'll Need

Barrel-shaped plastic container

2 wood blocks (1-cubic-inch)

2 cup hooks (1½-inch)

3-oz. lead free fishing sinker

Key ring (1-inch-diameter)

No. 64 rubber band

Drill with ⅛-inch bit

1. Drill centered holes in the lid, the bottom of the container, and partway into both wood blocks.

2. Feed a hook through the inside of the lid and screw it into one block; repeat on the bottom. Both hooks should face the inside of the jug.

3. Thread the sinker on the key ring; tie the rubber band to the key ring.

4. Loop the rubber band onto the hooks and screw on the lid.

5. Roll the jug on the floor. When it stops, marvel at what happens next.

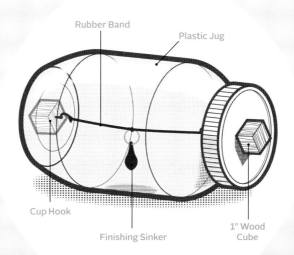

Rubber Band

Plastic Jug

Cup Hook

Finishing Sinker

1" Wood Cube

MAKE IT!

Adult Supervision Required!

Backyard Water Rocket

Get an adult to help you, and turn any afternoon into a blast with this easy-to-build water rocket.

Why It Matters

Humans are fascinated with sending objects into flight—planes, helicopters, parasails, and spacecraft. Using science, you can even send a water rocket high into the air. It all depends on how airtight your seal remains until friction is defeated and the stopper flies off, launching the rocket into flight. Engineer your own water rocket using Newton's third law of motion for an afternoon of wet fun!

What You'll Need

Electric drill with $\frac{1}{16}$-, $\frac{5}{32}$-, and $\frac{1}{4}$-inch bits

1 No. 4 size rubber stopper (1-inch-long, 1-inch diameter at the fat end)

1 piece copper tubing (8-inch length of $\frac{3}{16}$-inch outside diameter)

Bicycle pump with inflation needle

Heavy card stock

1 plastic bottle (2-liter)

Duct tape

1 drinking straw, minimum $\frac{1}{4}$-inch diameter

4 wood blocks (1-inch-square)

$\frac{1}{2}$-inch plywood board (12 to 16 inches square)

$\frac{1}{4}$-inch threaded steel rod (18 inches long)

4 nuts ($\frac{1}{4}$-inch)

2 washers ($\frac{1}{4}$-inch hole, 1-inch diameter)

Glue or $1\frac{1}{4}$-inch wood screws

Make the Stopper Assembly

1. Drill a $\frac{1}{16}$-inch hole through the middle of the stopper.

2. Widen the hole by drilling the $\frac{5}{32}$-inch bit about $\frac{1}{2}$ inch into the top (wider part) of the stopper.

3. Insert the copper tubing into the $\frac{5}{32}$-inch hole.

4. Push the inflation needle into the hole in the bottom of the stopper so that it feeds into the copper tube.

Build the Rocket

5. Make fins from card stock; attach to the bottle with duct tape.

6. Tape the 8-inch drinking straw to the side of the bottle (oriented from top to bottom).

Build the Launchpad

7. Attach square blocks to the corners of the launch platform (plywood), using quick-setting glue or $1\frac{1}{4}$-inch wood screws.

8. Place the rocket in the center of the launch platform and mark the spot directly below the plastic straw.

9. Drill a $\frac{1}{4}$-inch hole through the mark; insert the steel rod into the hole, and fix in place with nuts and washers.

Prepare the Hydro-Pump Rocket for Launch

10. Attach the bicycle pump to the inflation needle.

11. Fill the bottle one-third full with water, below the top of the copper tube.

12. Push the stopper assembly firmly into the bottle's mouth.

13. Invert the rocket and slide the soda straw onto the rod.

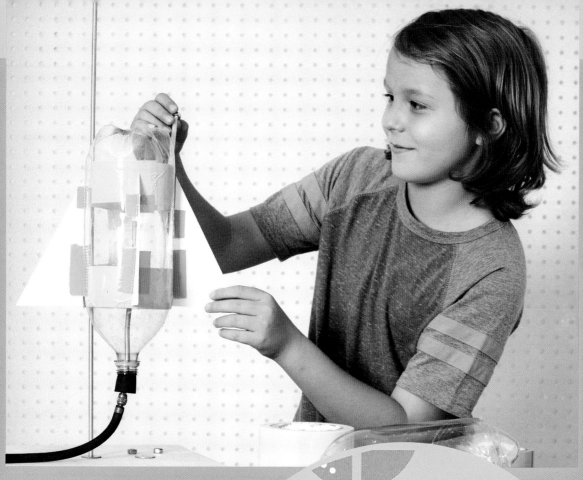

Launch the Rocket

14. Pump air into the rocket. The amount of pressure required to fire the rocket will vary depending on how clean the seal between the rubber stopper and the rocket is, and how firmly the stopper is placed.

15. After several pumps, the pressure inside the rocket will be great enough to overcome the friction holding the stopper in place. Now comes the cool part, as the stopper releases from the rocket and the rocket launches high into the air, shooting a trail of water behind it. Zoom!

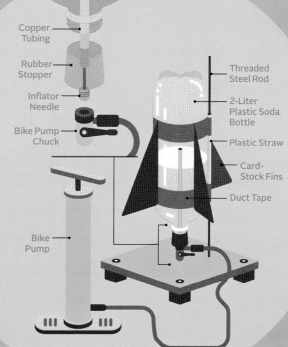

Copper Tubing

Rubber Stopper

Inflator Needle

Bike Pump Chuck

Bike Pump

Threaded Steel Rod

2-Liter Plastic Soda Bottle

Plastic Straw

Card-Stock Fins

Duct Tape

MAKE IT!

Floating Ping-Pong Table

Create the perfect new toy to bring to the pool!

Why It Matters

Ping-Pong is already a fun sport, but imagine how much more challenging it can be to move in water while playing. By engaging in PVC cutting and fastening techniques, and the addition of pool noodles, you will have the perfect ping-pong table to level up your Ping-Pong skills!

What You'll Need

3 pool noodles

Aluminum corrugated plastic sheet: sign panel ¼- x 24- x 48-inch

4 PVC end caps (4½-inch)

2 No. 10-x 1-inch stainless-steel pan-head screws

1½-inch x 2-foot PVC pipe

1 roll of 5½-inch black mesh ribbon (michaels.com, Celebrate It ribbon No. 10217699)

Plastic Ping-Pong paddles and balls

Hand miter saw

Utility knife

Cordless drill

Hot-glue gun

1. Using a hand miter saw, cut two lengths of pool noodle to 24 inches and two to 48 inches.

2. Use a sharp utility knife to slit each pool noodle down its center.

3. Find the centerline of the plastic sheet by measuring 24 inches in from the long end. Mark a point one inch in from either side on this line. With a cordless drill and a %4-inch twist bit, drill pilot holes in the two marks. Use the same bit to drill holes in the base of each end cap [A].

4. Place construction adhesive on the playing surface around the pilot holes and press each end cap in position. Drive a screw through the end cap and into the pilot hole [B].

5. To form the net posts, measure and mark two pieces of PVC pipe to three inches long. Crosscut them on the miter saw [C]. Press each one into an end cap mounted to the table.

6. Cut a piece of black mesh ribbon to 27 inches long and three inches wide. Wind a little ribbon around one of the net posts, then use a hot-glue gun to attach the ribbon to the post. Extend the ribbon to the other side of the table. Wind the ribbon around the opposite post, and glue it in place [D]. Press another end cap on top of each post.

7. Test-fit the pool noodles to the edges of the game board. Once you're sure they fit, glue each one to the board with construction adhesive.

8. Drill ¼-inch-diameter drain holes near each corner of the playing surface.

Hot-Air Balloon Simulator

Take this activity outside and send objects soaring! Since you'll be working with fire, make sure you have an adult to help you too.

Why It Matters

One way to get a bird's-eye view of your town is to ride in a hot-air balloon. Of course, there's a lot that goes into it—filling a hot-air balloon, changing altitude, changing direction, etc. How about we simulate the science of how one takes flight? Simply put, it's all about the air density. Let's start small with an envelope and work our way up!

The Basics

HOW TO FILL A HOT-AIR BALLOON

First, you have to fill the deflated balloon with air, says Sam Parks, a 30-year veteran hot-air balloon pilot. After unfolding the balloon so it lies flat on its side, pilots use a huge fan to partially inflate it with cool morning air. Next, they heat the air with propane burners that put out 15 to 20 million Btu of heat.

Like any gas, air expands when heated, becoming less dense and rising above denser elements. When the air inside the balloon gets to 100 degrees above the temperature outside the balloon, the balloon lifts into the air. Once full, the typical modern-day hot-air balloon carries about 80,000 cubic feet of air. That's approximately the equivalent of 80,000 basketballs!

HOW TO CHANGE ALTITUDE

To increase the balloon's altitude, the pilot fires one of the balloon's two propane burners to heat the air inside the balloon and raise its pressure. To bring down the hot air balloon, the pilot can either wait for the balloon to cool off by itself, or open a vent called the parachute valve and release some air to lower the temperature instantly.

HOW TO CHANGE DIRECTION

The balloon itself has no steering mechanism. Instead, pilots use air currents, which typically travel in different directions, based on altitude. So, if you increase or decrease altitude, you change the direction the balloon is blown. It's not an exact science, which means balloons usually can't land in the same spot they took off from unless you're in Albuquerque.

WHY ALBUQUERQUE?

There's a reason why every year more than 350 balloons fly in the Albuquerque International Balloon Fiesta, and it's because of very cool science! The festival's spectacular flights rely on a weather phenomenon called the Albuquerque Box. At higher altitudes, the winds blow consistently to the north. At lower altitudes, they blow consistently to the south. That balance gives balloon pilots better control, and often they can land in nearly the same spot they took off from.

Now, grab an adult and let's simulate this concept by lighting an object on fire! It's also best to do this outside as it can be flammable and the object will rise quickly.

What You'll Need

An envelope (a balloon's bag)

A pair of scissors

A small nonflammable dish or plate (ceramic works well)

Matches or a lighter

1. Take your envelope and shape it into a cylinder for the molecules to gather and expand.

2. Light the top of the cylinder on fire. Light it all the way around. What happens? Did it take flight?

3. Once it's lightweight ash, it gains lift and flies up due to the rising hot air currents. When it cools, it should descend back down slowly.

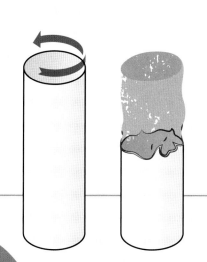

TIP

Try different, lightweight, flammable materials to see what works best— paper napkin, tissue, empty tea bag, or paper.

WIND

TIP

Make sure your sails fully fill with air by catching the air downwind (wind is behind the boat). If wind hits the side, the boat will still move, but not necessarily in the direction you desire.

A

B

C

E

F

D

G

H

I

LIFT

MAKE IT!

A Wind-Powered Boat

Tap into your inner sailor for this activity!

Why It Matters

A sail full of wind forms an airfoil and propels the boat with lift, the way a plane's wings does (except across water, rather than into the air). The work of sailing is to position, or trim, the sails to maximize lift in the direction you want to go.

How Wind Moves a Boat

Once you've raised the sails using the lines, called halyards (A), they're trimmed using the sheets (D), which pivot the boom (E) between the port (left) and starboard (right) sides of the boat. On a two-sail boat like this one (called a sloop), the emphasis is on the mainsail (B), the sail nearer the stern (H), which is the rearmost, or aft, part of the boat. The smaller jib (C), nearer the bow (F), at the fore, also pivots—but as a new sailor you'll be focused on the mainsail.

The basic idea is to use the tiller (G) to move the rudder (I) and angle the boat so that it is perpendicular to the wind. Use the sheets to angle the mainsail so it fills with wind. In the bowing airfoil shape, air moving over the longer, curved side moves faster than air flowing by the other side, generating lift.

Now that you know how to sail a boat, let's engineer one powered by wind. Let the engineering design process guide you when tackling this challenge.

Think about the Base, or Hull, of Your Boat.

Will it be strong enough to withstand fierce winds or water without falling apart? Will the weight affect the resistance? How big will it be? Do some research online to discover how boats are made. Why do some have a curved bottom? Does that help them glide across the water faster?

Don't Forget the Sails. Remember that the airfoil created by the sail moves the boat forward. You may need to trim the sails to maximize their lift and direction. A mast will help secure it. The mainsail at the back of the boat is key for new sailors. Decide what tools are best to use.

Design Your Steerage. Angle your boat to meet wind at the proper spot. What will you use for wind energy? Will you blow on it or use a hair dryer or electric fan?

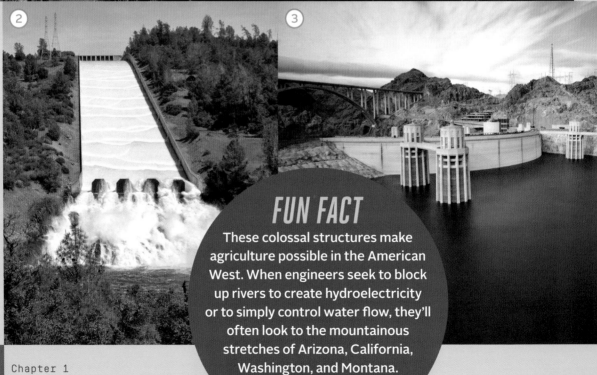

FUN FACT

These colossal structures make agriculture possible in the American West. When engineers seek to block up rivers to create hydroelectricity or to simply control water flow, they'll often look to the mountainous stretches of Arizona, California, Washington, and Montana.

The Lowdown on Dams

Whether you're on a family road trip or preparing for a spot on Jeopardy!, it's important to get familiar with the nation's most monumental dams.

Why It Matters

Dams are huge architectural wonders primarily made of concrete. Dams back up rivers in order to make hydroelectricity or manage the flow of water. The science and engineering of dams is no small undertaking. Consider the science and engineering required to build an effective dam. Think about the consequences if they break down. The architectural design is key to make sure it holds. Take a tour of eight of the most noteworthy, and then try your hand at some trivia about our nation's most famous dams!

1. Theodore Roosevelt Dam
ROOSEVELT, ARIZONA

The Theodore Roosevelt Dam was originally constructed between 1905 and 1911 to halt the wayward flow of the Salt River and irrigate the harsh Arizona desert, making it more amenable to farming.

The structure is named for President Theodore Roosevelt, who was instrumental in passing the Federal Reclamation Act of 1902, which funded irrigation projects in the West. At completion, the resulting reservoir—Theodore Roosevelt Lake—came in at 526,875 acre-feet of water, making it the largest constructed lake at the time.

2. Oroville Dam
FEATHER RIVER, CALIFORNIA

Forget heavy concrete for a moment—the tallest dam in the U.S. doesn't need it. About 70 miles north of Sacramento, along the Feather River in the Sierra Nevada foothills, this earthfill dam rises 770 feet tall and, at the base, has a reach of three-quarters of a mile.

This mound of earth contains the Lake Oroville reservoir, which offers drinking water, water-based recreation, and hydroelectric power while minimizing flood damage. It was officially dedicated in 1968, seven years after the start of construction—with one giant train wreck during construction that halted all progress for a week. The Oroville has stood as the country's tallest dam for more than 50 years.

3. Hoover Dam
COLORADO RIVER, ARIZONA/NEVADA

Built between 1931 and 1935, this dam was easily the most expensive engineering project in the United States at the time and became the tallest dam in the country at 726 feet tall. Still the second-tallest dam overall, and the tallest concrete dam, it required 91.8 billion cubic feet of concrete to create the arch-gravity dam with its 600-foot-wide base and 6.6 million tons in weight.

The Hoover Dam holds back the Colorado River and straddles the border between Arizona and Nevada near Boulder City, Nevada, a town originally created for the project's workers.

4. Grand Coulee Dam
SPOKANE, WASHINGTON

The Grand Coulee Dam may not be the tallest at 550 feet, but the seriousness of this 1942-built dam outside of Spokane, Washington, comes from its sheer size. With over 12 million cubic yards of concrete,

CONTINUED ON NEXT PAGE!

The Lowdown on Dams

the Grand Coulee Dam spans the Columbia River for nearly a full mile, backing up Franklin D. Roosevelt Lake reservoir nearly to Canada.

With 21 billion kilowatt-hours of electricity annually, Grand Coulee creates the most hydroelectric power of any dam in the United States.

5. Dworshak Dam
OROFINO, IDAHO

It took roughly seven years to build what would become the third-tallest dam in the nation. Since 1973, Dworshak has sat a few miles outside of Orofino, Idaho, blocking up the Clearwater River and creating the Dworshak Reservoir.

Despite its impressiveness, the 717-foot-tall dam was never a popular project. Dworshak has been saddled with controversy—1990s-era expansion approvals were rescinded for disrupting the natural wildlife of the area.

6. Fort Peck Dam
GLASGOW, MONTANA

At over 21,000 feet in length, and with a base width of 3,500 feet, Fort Peck is the largest hydraulically filled dam in the world.

In 1940, the United States Army Corps of Engineers crews created the New Deal-era dam by pumping sediment from the bottom of the Missouri River and mixing it with rock and natural materials. Fort Peck Lake rests behind the dam. Hydroelectric generation started in 1943, complete with an Art Deco spillway. It can pump out a

staggering 250,000 cubic feet of water per second.

7. Glen Canyon Dam
PAGE, ARIZONA

At 710 feet tall, this concrete arch-gravity dam near Page, Arizona, fills a canyon-heavy region on the upper Colorado River with water. Under construction from 1956 to 1966, the dam forms Lake Powell behind it, the second-largest constructed reservoir in the United States

Conceived of before the Hoover Dam, but built later, Glen Canyon helps manage water distribution in the river's basin and, along with hydroelectricity generation, can help hold onto runoff for lean water years while ensuring fewer droughts for those downstream.

8. Ashfork-Bainbridge Steel Dam
JOHNSON CANYON, ARIZONA

Almost everything about the Ashfork-Bainbridge Steel Dam is different from a typical dam in the West. Not only is it one of only two major dams in the nation using steel—the first of the two—this 1898-completed structure was not meant to generate hydroelectricity like its counterparts.

Owned by the Atchison, Topeka, and Santa Fe Railway, the dam moved water via piping from Johnson Canyon into the town of Ash Fork, supplying a water stop for steam locomotives. The dam contains 24 curved steel plates and runs 184

feet long and 46 feet high. It's been holding back water since before Arizona, the state where it resides, was officially part of the Union.

Now test your knowledge of the amazing dams in the United States!

Trivia Questions:

1. Which dam is the first of only two major dams in the United States to use steel?

2. Which dam was created to enable farming through irrigation of a desert region?

3. Which dam creates more hydroelectric power than any other dam in the United States?

4. How many watts of electricity does the dam in number three generate per year?

5. What is the largest hydraulically filled dam in the world?

6. Needing 91.8 billion cubic feet of concrete, which dam weighs 6.6 million tons?

7. Using hydroelectricity generation, which dam assists with water distribution management in the river's basin?

8. How does the answer to number 7 assist the dam's community in water conservation efforts?

9. Out of all operating dams in the United States, which one stands the tallest at 770 feet?

10. Which dam became less popular and had its expansion rights revoked due to its effect on the surrounding area's natural wildlife?

Answers on page 220

④

Take It One Step Further

See if you can match each dam with the proper location in the United States as described in the article. Then try to find it on a map of the United States by first identifying the correct state in which the dam is located. Then plan a visit!

⑤

⑥

⑦

⑧

MAKE IT!
The Perfect Paper Airplane

Here's how to make a paper plane that's guaranteed to dominate your living room skies, with pointers from Barnaby Wainfan, a technical fellow and aerodynamicist at aerospace and defense company, Northrop Grumman.

Why It Matters

This is a project that appears simple at first, but is very complex when you want your aviation creation to fly a bit further than a few feet. So, what are the right folds, cuts, and edges needed to create the perfect paper plane? What science and engineering skills do you need to determine how far and how fast your paper airplane will fly given specific parameters? What can you do to increase your flight time? Let's find out!

Start by folding the paper in half down the center of the plane. Cut along the perimeter to get a perfectly symmetrical aircraft.

Now fold the wings down along line No. 1. Then grab the tail in the center and fold it in the opposite direction along the same line, so it extends above the wings. Next, fold down along line No. 2. At the seam where the wings meet use a piece of adhesive tape to hold them together. Add a standard paper clip beside the nose to balance the weight of the thinner nose with the plane's wide wings. Lastly, fold the flaps up along line No. 3.

After a test flight, troubleshoot by adjusting those folds. If the plane nosedives, bend the rear flaps to make them more vertical. If it swoops up and then dives straight down, flatten them.

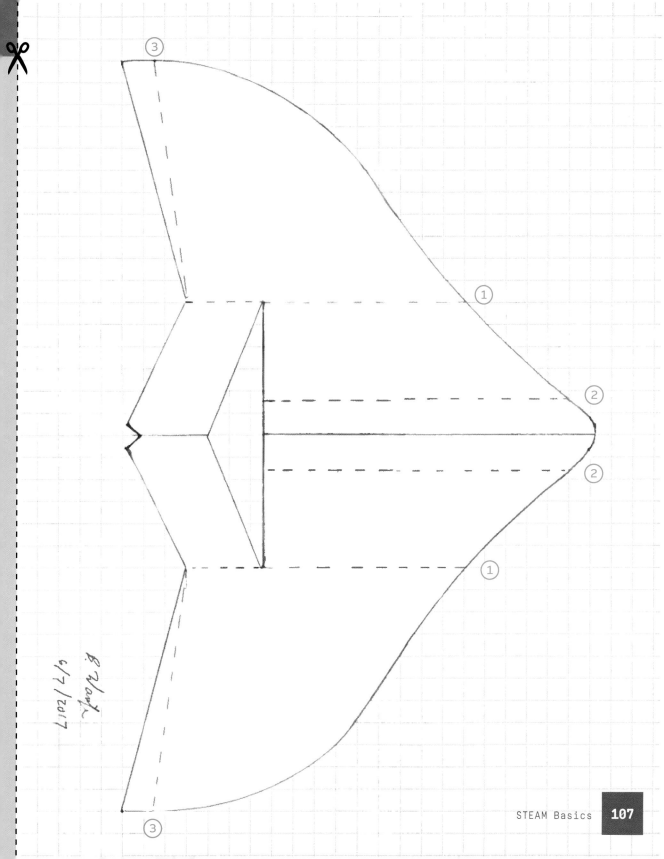

③

①

②

②

①

③

𝐵 𝒲𝑎𝓈𝒽
6/7/2017

CHAPTER 2

Building on that Maker Mindset

Now that you know the basics, the possibilities are endless. Continue asking questions and testing your limits. Are you up for it? Here we go!

Monster Mask

Make your own monster mask to create a disguise or impress your friends!

Why It Matters

Use artistic design skills to make your mask truly one of a kind. Do you like being a detective? Use science tools and resources such as safety goggles or a magnifying glass to turn your eye pieces into spyware by making them into binoculars. Will your mask hold a hidden feature? You decide!

What You'll Need

Hot-glue gun

1 pair flexible plastic safety goggles

1 brightly colored bungee cord

1 cleaning pad

1 string mop

2 PVC reducer fittings (1½-inch)

Scissors

1. Use a hot-glue gun to fasten the reducer fittings to the goggles.

2. Cut the bungee cord to length, then wrap and glue the cords around each fitting, gluing the ends to prevent fraying.

3. Use scissors to cut the cleaning pad into two arch-shaped "eyebrows." Fasten them above the fittings with hot-melt glue.

4. Cut off a section of the string mop and glue its supporting band to the goggles' top shield.

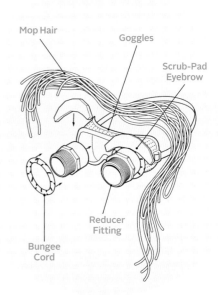

Mop Hair

Goggles

Scrub-Pad Eyebrow

Reducer Fitting

Bungee Cord

MAKE IT!
Your Own Bird's Nest

Here's an activity that lets you have free reign over materials and design. Get creative!

Why It Matters

In the previous chapter, we learned that birds are resilient, adaptable creatures (page 16). Based on their needs, they build nests in bushes, on the ground, in trees, or on rocky ledges with materials at their disposal. Sharpen your scientific observation skills by analyzing birds in their habitat, use math to determine adequate measurements, and engineer a nest outfitted with the right building materials.

Observe. Do some bird watching. Research is important, but you may stumble upon key findings seeing their habits up close. When you're ready to build, you can use the internet to check if you're on the right track.

Define Parameters. What kind of bird do you wish to attract with your nest? Figure out size, weight, and habits so you know exactly what needs to go into your design. Where would you place your creation and why?

Think About Materials. Some natural materials to consider: twigs, mud, clay, ferns, mulch, and leaves. Synthetic materials like string, thread, bits of felt, cotton balls, or fake moss might work well too.

Build It. Once you have your materials on hand and have a definite design in mind, you can start creating your nest. Set it out at the location of your choice and wait to see if birds come flocking!

TIP

Pick materials based on the bird's needs. Do they require camouflage against predators, insulators like grass, or rocks/acorns to keep cool? How will you keep it together?

MAKE IT!

Book Light

Racking your brain for the best way to light up your bedroom fort? Learn about basic electricity and soldering in this fun and useful project.

Why It Matters

If your idea of a cozy night is reading a book under a tent you made with bedding draped over your desk chairs, it's important to have a well-lit space so you don't strain your eyes. Use engineering and circuitry skills to design a book light. Add some technology to the mix and make your indoor camping trip even more enjoyable.

What You'll Need

1 piece lightweight scrap wood, about ¼-inch-thick

1 Adafruit ADA783 coin-cell battery pack and switch

2 feet low-wattage wire, 18- to 22-gauge

Electrical tape

1 mini clothespin

1 white Uxcell 6-volt diode

1 plastic Easter egg

2 coin-cell batteries (3-volt)

Wood glue

Miter saw, jigsaw, or handsaw

Coping saw

Drill

Hot-glue gun

Soldering gun

1. Crosscut the piece of scrap wood to produce a 3- by ¼-inch wooden base. Mark the curved sides with a pencil, and use a coping saw or jigsaw to cut the curves.

2. Use a ³⁄₃₂-inch twist drill bit to make the two holes, spaced about ½ inch apart near the top of the base.

3. Center the battery pack approximately ¼ inch up from the base's bottom edge. Use a hot-glue gun to attach the battery pack to the base.

4. Cut the wires coming from the battery pack to 1 inch long and strip ¼-inch of insulation from the ends. Cut two 12-inch pieces of the low-wattage wire and strip the ends. Solder the battery-pack wires to the low-wattage wires. Once it cools, wrap the joint with electrical tape.

5. Flip the base so the battery pack is facing down. Use wood glue to attach the clothespin to the top of the base edge.

6. Run the low-wattage wire from the bottom of the battery pack under the base, up to the clothespin, and through the two holes. Pull the wires through the holes, then twist them together to form the neck of the light.

7. Use a ³⁄₃₂-inch bit to bore two holes in the Easter egg. Feed the wires from the diode through these holes. With the battery pack switched to the "On" position, hold the two diode wires to the electrical leads to determine the correct orientation to make the diode illuminate. When you've got it right, solder the wires to the LED leads.

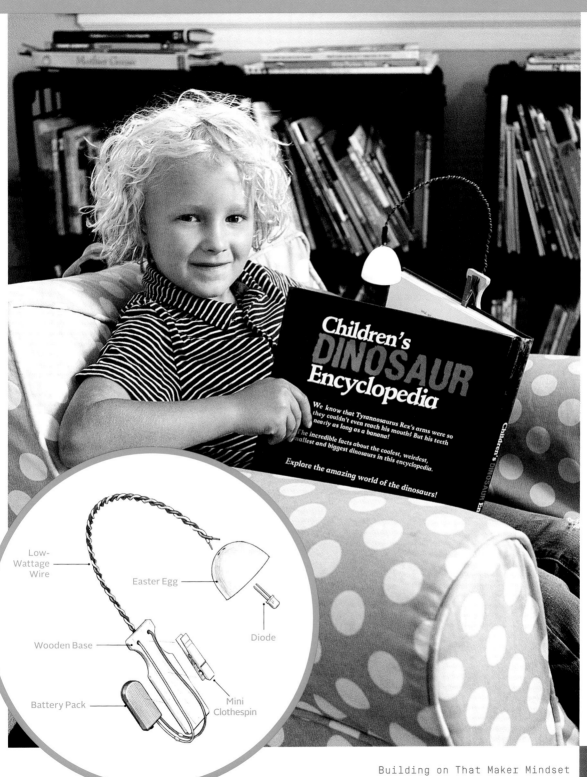

Children's DINOSAUR Encyclopedia

We know that Tyrannosaurus Rex's arms were so they couldn't even reach his mouth? But his teeth nearly as long as a banana!

The incredible facts about the coolest, weirdest, smallest and biggest dinosaurs in this encyclopedia.

Explore the amazing world of the dinosaurs!

Low-Wattage Wire

Easter Egg

Diode

Wooden Base

Battery Pack

Mini Clothespin

Ice Lantern

Learn the scientific properties while building a lantern for an imaginary ice hotel!

Why It Matters

In science, we use basic circuitry to create closed circuits to run a continuous path of electricity. If the circuit is broken, as in an open circuit, then the bulb will not light. Apply these same concepts to a lantern. First, research the difference between conductors and insulators to know what will carry your electricity from its power source (battery) to the load (bulb), and then build from there!

What You'll Need

1 (or more) oversize ice cube tray

Various ice cube fillers (leaves, rocks, tiny toys, food coloring, etc.)

1 pipette (a small baster)

1 LED light

1 baking sheet

Aluminum foil

1. Make a bunch of zany oversize ice cubes. (You can find the silicone trays at kitchen stores.) Put anything you want in the cubes—we used cereal, food coloring, pebbles, small toys, leaves, and other stuff. We even froze a length of string between two cubes to be used as a handle.

2. Line a baking sheet with aluminum foil—this is your building surface. Set a bowl of water next to your work area. Now you can start building your ice structure, using the cubes as bricks. To affix one cube to another, use the pipette to squirt some water where the two cubes meet. The cubes will freeze the water, creating a bond. Our base was a three-by-three square.

3. Build the walls up from the base, leaving a chute in the center for the LED light. Try to match cubes that

have flat sides for better bonds. If you've planned for a handle (like we did with the string), remember to save those cubes for the top. When you're happy with your lantern, place the whole thing (carefully) in the freezer to solidify the bonds and strengthen the structure.

4. Drop your LED light into the center and watch the lantern light up!

TIP

Before you start building, make enough room in your freezer to accommodate your lantern when it's ready for a final freeze.

MAKE IT!
Your Own Emoji Language

Here's a fun way to leave your friends coded messages.

Why It Matters

Egyptians communicated using hieroglyphics—they documented their history, engaged internationally, and enhanced their culture with simple images that give a wealth of knowledge. With today's technological advancements, there are a lot more ways that we communicate with one another. With a little art, science, and technology, let's see if we can be effective in communicating with friends by creating your own picture-based language.

Learn About Hieroglyphs. Do some online research to find out how they work. What do the symbols represent? What made it easier to use them in place of writing out the words?

Examine How You Communicate with Friends. Do you find yourself using contractions or acronyms to make texting faster? Do you use emojis to illustrate your thoughts more quickly?

Think about the Most Common Messages You Send Your Friends. Is there a way you can use emojis to string together a shorter message? Keep a log of everything you create.

For example:
Symbol = Message
Symbol + Symbol + Symbol = Message

You may find that you will also need to create some form of picture-based alphabet for those words that don't directly translate through pictures.

Take It One Step Further

Create a journal and log your day in the language you created. What will cultures of the future be able to learn from your language? Will they learn about what was important to you and how you lived? What will you document for history?

TIP

Think about common emojis on a computer keyboard, such as animals, facial expressions, gestures, modes of transportation, habitats, seasons, food, etc. Use a combination of these to create new forms of modern symbols. Get inspired!

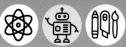
MAKE IT!
Battle Bots

Using a simple motor, battery, and toothbrush, you are well on your way to designing your first robot—motorized creatures that scurry across the table!

Why It Matters

Battle Bots are simple things, miniature robots like the ones you see fighting on TV, only a lot less destructive—and just as much fun! Use your circuitry and technology skills to make a simple robot, then tie in your creative art skills to bring it to life! Turn it into an insect and add wings, or create one that can paint in different patterns. Let your imagination run wild!

What You'll Need

1 toothbrush

1 battery holder (RadioShack item No. 2700009)

1 DC micro vibration motor (3-volt) (RadioShack item No. 2730107)

1 button battery (3-volt)

Craft paper

Card stock

Vise

Coping saw

Soldering iron

Sharpie

Hot-glue gun

1. Clamp a toothbrush in a vise and cut off the head with a coping saw. Discard the handle of the toothbrush.

2. To connect the leads from the vibration motor to the ones on the battery holder, use a soldering iron to melt a small ball of solder onto the end of each motor lead. One at a time, touch each lead to the battery holder and apply heat with the iron.

3. Use a Sharpie to draw wings on a piece of craft paper. Cut out the shape with scissors.

4. Apply a glob of hot glue to the back of the toothbrush toward one end of the head.

5. Before the glue hardens, press the battery holder into it.

6. Repeat the procedure to glue the vibrating motor near the other end of the toothbrush head. Be careful

not to get glue on any of the motor's moving parts.

7. Slide a battery into the battery holder, but keep it separated from the contact point with a thick piece of paper or card stock. To make the bot go, just withdraw the slip of paper. To make it stop, slide the paper back in.

8. Use the hot-glue gun to glue the paper wings on the bot, either on the motor or the space between it and the battery.

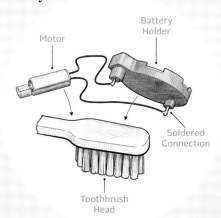

Motor

Battery Holder

Soldered Connection

Toothbrush Head

TRY IT!
Coded Hidden Treasure

Let's build some algorithms!

Why It Matters

Coding is a language that enables programming to take place. While you might not consider becoming a robotics or software engineer, plenty of other careers now use coding. Want to launch your own fashion line? Dream of opening your own restaurant? Create code to make it easier for people to order online. Robots are even designed to perform and assist in high-tech surgeries! And these are all possible by stringing a set of instructions called algorithm that tell a device what it needs to do. With a little technology, science, and math, you'll be coding in no time!

What You'll Need

Paper

Colored pencils

Your choice of "treasure"

Your Challenge:

Code a Friend to Find Buried Treasure in Your Backyard.

1. On a blank sheet of paper, draw a map of your backyard. Be sure to include any important landmarks such as a treehouse, playground equipment, pond, or fence.

2. Mark your cardinal directions.

3. Consider creating a key to make some symbols of repeated objects like obstacles (rocks).

4. Make an X to mark the spot of your buried treasure.

5. On a separate piece of paper, code your friend from a specific starting point to the X without drawing a path. Use coding blocks to build your algorithm.

6. Give your map and coding directions to a friend. Then turn them loose in your backyard. Are they able to find your buried treasure or do you need to iterate and debug your code to make it work?

★	When Run
↑	Move Forward
↻	Turn Right 90°
↺	Turn Left 90°
◄►◄►	Loop (x)
🥄	Dig
🌱	Bring to Surface

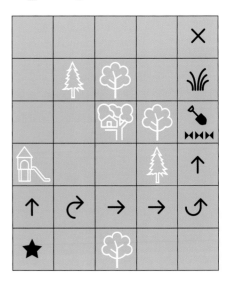

TIP

Always start with your "When Run" block. When you are finished, end with your "Run" block to actually run the code. For example: When Run, Move Forward, Move Forward, Turn Right 90 Degrees, Move Forward, Move Forward, Turn Left 90 Degrees, Move Forward. Use a Loop (X3) to Dig. Then Bring to Surface.

What You'll Need

4 lengths of 1 x 2 pine (6 feet long) (legs)

2 plywood pieces (¼-inch thick, 18- x 48-inches)

46-inch length of 1 x 2 pine (crossbeam)

14 No. 8 wood screws (1½-inch)

2 eyebolts with wingnuts (⁵⁄₁₆- x 4-inches)

6 washers, 1-inch outer diameter, ⅜-inch hole

4 eye lags (¼- x 2-inches)

4 carabiners (2-inches)

2 chains (32-inches-long)

Funnel, 6-inch top diameter

Two rubber grommets, ½-inch inner diameter

6-inch old garden hose or plastic tubing

24-inch length of rope

Fender washer, 2-inch outside diameter, ½-inch hole

4-foot surgical tubing

Drill

MAKE IT!

Water Balloon Launcher

Let the water balloon war begin!

Why It Matters

When launching the balloon, think about the trajectory or path it will take. Having a big balloon filled to the brim with water may give a bigger splash when broken, but, due to air resistance, it's not going to travel very far when launched. The angle at which you launch will also have an effect on how far it travels. Challenge your friends to a friendly contest, and then put your science skills to work!

Build the Frame.

1. Drill a $5/16$-inch hole in the center of the 2-inch side of each leg, 3 inches from one end.

2. On the narrow side of two legs, mark 12 inches from the end opposite the holes. Align the bottom of a plywood piece with the marks, hold the outer edges of the plywood and the legs flush, and drill three $1/8$-inch pilot holes on each side, $3/8$ inch from the edge. Screw the plywood to the legs. Mark the legs 6 inches from the top of the plywood. Line up the bottom edge of the remaining piece of plywood on the marks and fasten it to the legs. This is the launcher's front.

3. Lay the other two legs on a level surface, parallel and with the outer edges $46\frac{1}{2}$ inches apart. Mark the narrow side of each leg 18 inches from the bottom, line up the crossbeam with the marks, and fasten it with one screw on each side. This is the back.

4. Connect the two assemblies by fitting the narrower one inside the other, lining up the $5/16$-inch holes and putting the eyebolts through the holes, with the eye on the inside. Use three washers per side, one each between the eye and the inside leg, the two legs, and the wingnut and the outer leg.

5. Screw an eye lag bolt into each leg, 36 inches from bottom. Use the carabiners and chains to connect the eyebolts.

Make the Water Balloon Holder— And Get Launching!

6. Drill two $\frac{1}{2}$-inch holes opposite each other into the funnel, 1 inch from top; fit grommets into the holes. Slide a 6-inch piece of hose onto rope; push rope's ends through the narrow end of the funnel and hole in the fender washer. Tie the ends together.

7. Tie two 24-inch lengths of surgical tubing through the grommets and the eyebolts. Stand behind the frame, grasp the balloon holder's handle, and pull down at an angle. Load the funnel with a water balloon—and let it fly!

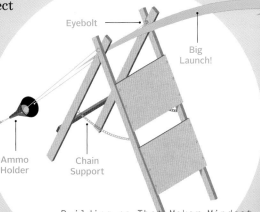

Eyebolt

Big Launch!

Ammo Holder

Chain Support

Ping-Pong Cannon

Level up your Nerf gun shooting skills after making this fun project!

Why It Matters

Engineer a Ping-Pong cannon with a little science and correct math measurements. Using PVC for the barrel greatly improves accuracy. Power is limited only by how much air you can pump into the chamber. This Ping-Pong cannon can fire a ball up to 70 feet, but not with so much force that it will cause injury. You could have some minor damage if used indoors though (we broke a glass!), so maybe set up some empty cans outdoors for target practice instead!

What You'll Need

1 PVC pipe (1½x 24 inches)

1 tubeless tire valve (part TR415, .625 rim hole)

1 PVC slip cap (1½ inches)

1 PVC ball valve (1½ inches)

1 peel-and-stick Velcro roll (¾- x 60 inches)

1 package PVC glue and primer

1 package Ping-Pong balls or foam practice golf balls

1 travel bike pump

Holesaw or spade bit

1. After crosscutting the PVC pieces to length, secure the 8-inch piece to your workbench by inserting the jaw of a clamp into the pipe. Use a holesaw or spade bit running at a slow and constant speed to make a ⅝-inch hole for the tubeless tire valve, 2½ inches from the end of the pipe.

2. Slip the tubeless tire valve through the end of the pipe and work its stem up through the hole you just drilled. Pull the valve into position with pliers, being careful not to damage the threads. You won't need glue, but you will need to ensure that the upper flange of the valve is completely outside the pipe.

3. Apply PVC primer followed by PVC glue to the end of the pipe closer to the valve. Do the same on the end cap. Press the parts together, then give the end cap a small twist to distribute glue into the joint.

4. Lubricate the ball valve with a few drops of oil.

5. Apply primer and glue to the mating surfaces of the ball valve, one end of the 8-inch pipe, and one end of the 6-inch pipe. Press the parts together and twist slightly to distribute the glue. Make sure you twist far enough that the tire valve isn't directly in line with the ball-valve handle.

6. Run a length of peel-and-stick Velcro around the end cap and another between the ball valve and the tire valve. Wrap corresponding pieces of Velcro to the bike pump, the same distance apart as the Velcro on the cannon. Attach the pump head to the tire valve. To operate, pump as much air as you can into the cannon, then turn the ball valve to fire!

CONTINUED ON NEXT PAGE!

Ball valve

8" Chamber

6" Firing tube

Velcro
straps

Bike pump

Velcro
straps

Ping Pong Cannon

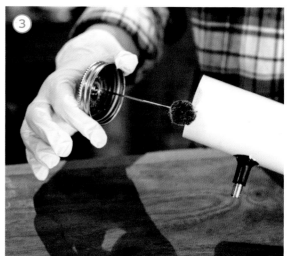

12"

24"

12"

Elbow

Spray
Nozzle

Tee

1 ½"

Hose
Connector

63"

Shut-Off
Valve

2"

Tee

Tee

2"

Hose
Connector

70"

20"

20"

Hose
Connector

End Cap

A Backyard Bike Wash

PVC is the perfect material for creating your own bike wash. It's lightweight, watertight, and not very expensive. Grab an adult assistant and get creative!

Why It Matters

Riding your bike through mud puddles is a fun activity, but cleaning it after? Not so much. Dumping buckets of water on it is only effective for singular parts of the bike. Here's a thought: Your parents run their vehicles through a car wash when they get dirty. How about making something similar for your bike? Use your science skills to adjust the water pressure. Make sure when you engineer the water pipes that you measure correctly to have tight seals. Then you can get muddy and have fun cleaning it up later too!

What You'll Need

Hacksaw

22½ feet PVC (¾-inch)

5 tee connectors

3 end caps

4 screw-on hose connectors (¾-inch)

2 elbows (90-degree)

1 shut-off valve (¾-inch)

2 screw-on lawn spray nozzles

1 strip Velcro

1. Make each foot of the bike wash by connecting two 20-inch pieces of PVC with a tee. One foot should be closed off with two end caps. The other needs an end cap on one side and a hose connector on the other (to connect the hose from the house).

2. On the foot with two end caps, insert a 70-inch piece of PVC in the open end of the tee. Place a 90-degree elbow on the end.

3. Assemble the top bar by inserting a 12-inch piece into the elbow in step two. Insert a tee into the end of that, followed by a 24-inch piece of PVC and another tee, then another 12-inch piece and an elbow. In the perpendicular arm of each of the two tees, insert a 1½-inch piece of PVC, then a hose connector, then a spray nozzle.

4. On the other foot, insert a 2-inch piece of PVC into the open end of the tee. Add another tee to this piece of PVC. Screw a hose connector onto the perpendicular arm of the tee.

5. Above the tee add a 2-inch PVC valve, then a 63-inch PVC piece, which should connect to the elbow in the top bar.

6. Screw another hose onto the open connector. Add a piece of Velcro to the vertical post and spray nozzle.

Take It One Step Further

This setup includes an outlet for a hose and nozzles to spray-clean the really dirty parts of your bike. You can add more features such as a sprinkler spout or water cannon, but be careful: With too many components, you'll run out of water pressure. Whatever you build, after you attach the hose, turn on the water slowly, otherwise you might break some of your seals.

Unstoppable Airplane Launcher

Now that you've made the perfect paper plane (page 106), level up with a launcher sure to send it zooming farther than ever!

Why It Matters

Sure, you could fling your perfectly created paper airplane with your own human muscles, but it's much cooler to build a machine to do it for you. This design uses a few robotics parts, a little bit of soldering, and a few chops with the miter saw. In about an hour, you'll have a machine purposely built for some airplane flinging. You could even add your own artistic touches to name your design and patent it! Look at how you enhanced your paper airplane's aerodynamics to engage deeper science and make it fly even farther.

What You'll Need

- 1-inch x 3-inch x 4-foot poplar project board
- 2 3-volt electric motors (Lowe's item #364310, model #884477)
- Push-button on-off switch (RadioShack part #2750617)
- Holder for two AAA batteries (RadioShack part #2700398)
- 2 Solarbotics small rubber wheels with 2-mm shaft (bananarobotics.com part #BR010266)
- ⅜-inch x 2-inch carriage bolt, washer, wing nut
- 4-foot 20-gauge bell wire
- Miter saw
- Drill press
- ¹⁵⁄₁₆-inch spade drill bit
- Cordless drill
- ½-, ⅜-inch drill bits
- Wood glue
- Hot-glue gun
- Soldering gun
- Wire strippers
- Pliers

1. Use a miter saw to cut two 9-inch lengths and two 2-inch lengths from the poplar.

2. On one of the 9-inch boards, mark the position of the motor holes according to the diagram (opposite page). Bore the holes using a $^{15}/_{16}$-inch spade bit and a drill press or cordless drill.

3. Test-fit the motors and launch wheels to verify proper spacing. Use a hot-glue gun to fasten the motors so that their tops are flush with the top of the launch platform.

4. On the lower-left corner of the poplar piece with the launch wheels, use a drill and a ½-inch bit to make a hole for the push-button switch. Line the hole with a little hot glue and insert the switch. Use a ⅜-inch bit to make the bolt holes in the mounting blocks—the 2-inch lengths you cut in step 1—as shown in the diagram.

5. Cut two 9-inch lengths of wire and five 4-inch pieces. Strip ½ inch of insulation from each end.

6. Solder all of the connections in the schematic (above) except for the two on each motor. For those,

CONTINUED ON NEXT PAGE!

FUN FACT

John Collins holds the record for longest flight by a paper airplane. In 2012, the glider he designed landed after 226 feet, 10 inches. His launcher? Former quarterback Joe Ayoob.

Unstoppable Airplane Launcher

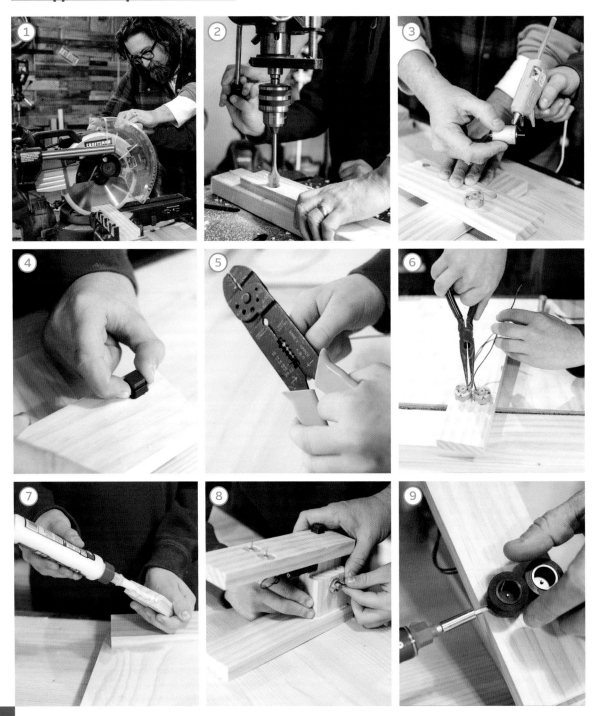

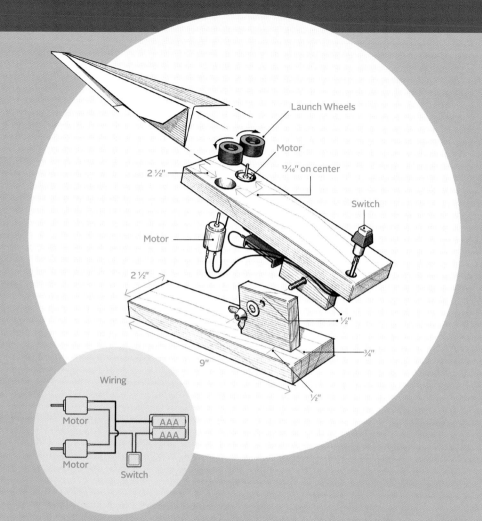

Launch Wheels

Motor

$^{13}/_{16}$" on center

2 ½"

Switch

Motor

2 ½"

½"

9"

¾"

½"

Wiring

Motor

AAA
AAA

Motor

Switch

bend the ends of the wires into hooks and insert them through the motor tabs. Insert batteries and test-drive the launch wheels. The motor on the right must turn clockwise; the left counterclockwise. If necessary, switch the positive and negative wires to reverse the wheels' direction. Once confirmed, crimp and solder the motor connections.

7. Hold the mounting blocks together and center them on the base according to the diagram. Make sure the bolt holes are on opposite edges. Spread some wood glue on the bottom of one block and the top of the other, then squeeze

the blocks between the base and the launch platform to glue them in place.

8. Use the hot-glue gun to fasten the battery holder to the launch platform. Insert a carriage bolt and washer through the holes in the mounting blocks. Tighten with a wing nut to connect the two halves of the launcher at a 45-degree angle.

9. Slip the rubber wheels over the top of the motor shafts. You should be able to fit five sheets of paper between the wheels. Tighten the set screw on the motor shaft.

Adult Supervision Required!

MAKE IT!

Ice Cream Maker

Every delicious treat is worth all the effort. And there's nothing more satisfying than making your own ice cream!

Why It Matters

Churning your own ice cream allows you to witness each step of the process in detail. So if you're up for the challenge, grab an adult to help you engineer your own ice cream machine. Pay attention to the math measurements so you get a proper fit, and use science to get your ice cream to the right consistency.

What You'll Need

2 oak boards (¾-inch x 2-inch x 2-feet)

1 oak board (¼-inch x 2-inch x 1-foot)

1 oak dowel (½-inch)

1 unused 1-gallon paint can, handle removed

4 round-head bolts and nuts (¼-20 x 1 ¼-inch)

2 washers (¼-inch x 1 ½-inch)

1 nylon spacer (0.562 x 0.375 x ½-inch)

1 food grade rubber grommet (¾-inch inside-diameter)

2 hanger bolts (#10-24 x 2-inch)

2 #10-24 wing nuts (#10-24)

1 decorative dresser knob

8-oz coffee can and lid

Nontoxic waterproof wood glue

Butcher-block oil

1. Crosscut the following parts to length from the ¾-inch stock: Cut part B to 4½ inches; cut part D to 2 inches; cut parts E and K to 8 inches, and cut part H to 2¾ inches. (It will later be cut into a parallelogram shape.) Complete part B by ripping it to ⅞-inch wide.

2. Crosscut the following parts to length from the ¼-inch stock: Cut part I to 4 inches, and cut part J to 2¾ inches. (It will also be cut into a parallelogram shape.)

3. Cut parts H and J into their finished lengths as a parallelogram shape. Set a miter saw to 30 degrees and cut these parts so their long sides measure 2 inches.

4. The crank arm and dowel rod (B and C) are one subassembly. They drive the paddle (H, I, and J), a separate subassembly. The trick is to allow the crank and paddle to spin freely while supporting it on top of the mixing can. The solution is surprisingly simple.

First crosscut the dowel rod to 7 inches long. Next, make the crank support by gluing parts D and E together. Center D on the length of E. When the glue has dried, bore a ½-inch hole centered on the width and length of these two parts. Now use an awl to mark the hole for the dowel rod (C) in the crank arm (B). Center the mark on the arm's width and 9⁄16 inch from its end. Bore a ½-inch hole on the

CONTINUED ON NEXT PAGE!

mark. Also drill the hole for the bolt that mounts the dresser knob (A). Its diameter depends on what you buy. You should position the hole so its center is about ½ inch from the end of the crank arm. Bolt the knob onto the arm. Lastly, bore the dowel-rod hole centered in part H.

5. Glue the dowel in the crank arm, and glue together the mixing paddle (parts H, I, and J). Slide the nylon spacer onto the dowel, and slip the dowel through the crank support (parts D and E glued together), but do not glue it. Cut a slightly oversize hole in the center of the coffee can lid (G), slip the grommet (F) and then the lid over the end of the dowel rod. Note: Do not glue the paddle onto the dowel rod just yet. You need to dry fit the paddle on the dowel to see if it turns freely in the coffee can.

6. Take one of the wood blocks that will become part K and mark its hole positions. It will become the template to drill the holes in both parts. Centered on the block's width, use the awl to mark both hole positions, 2 inches from each of the block's ends. Clamp the two part-K blocks together and drill a $^{15}/_{16}$-inch hole through both blocks at one end, and at the other end drill a ¼-inch hole. Use a sharp pencil and a straightedge to mark the diagonals on the end grain on the upper part of these blocks (the end nearest the

$^{15}/_{16}$-inch hole). Mark the center of the diagonals with an awl and bore a pilot hole on the mark using a $^{9}/_{64}$-inch twist drill bit. Apply a generous coating of butcher-block oil to these blocks, then turn the hanger bolts into their end grain, and let the oil dry. Fasten the blocks to the can through the top holes, then use a square held along the can's rim and the block's edge to align each block on the can's surface. Use the lower hole in each block to guide the drill bit to make the lower bolt hole through the paint can. Push the lower bolt through these holes and tighten the nut to each bolt.

7. Insert the coffee can into the paint can. Dry fit the paddle on the end of the dowel rod, and insert the paddle into the coffee can. The fit you're looking for is this: The plastic spacer below the crank arm should rest firmly on the top support, which should be supported by the blocks on the side of the can. When you crank the handle, the paddle should turn freely just above the bottom of the coffee can. If not, adjust the paddle position accordingly. Glue the paddle onto the end of the dowel rod and let the glue dry. Complete the project by applying a generous coating of butcher-block oil to the crank arm and paddle assembly. Allow the oil to thoroughly dry before making ice cream.

To Make Ice Cream

Layer a cup of rock salt and ice between the coffee can and the paint can. Pour cream into the coffee can and crank for about ten minutes or until the cream thickens to soft-serve consistency.

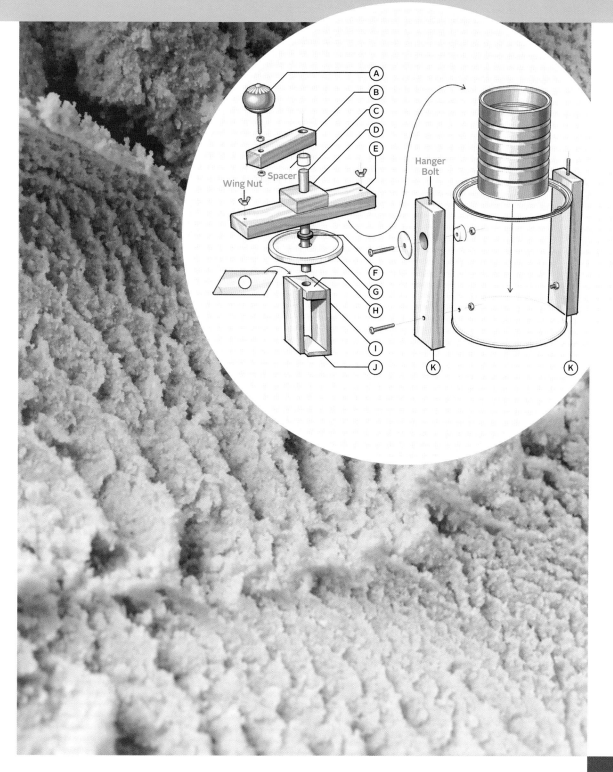

A

B

C

D

E

Spacer

Wing Nut

Hanger
Bolt

F

G

H

I

J

K

K

TRY IT!
Noodle Art

This is an activity where playing with your food is absolutely called for, so get an adult to help you boil some pasta and let's get creative!

Why It Matters

Pasta is a great material to work with. Not only is it delicious when it's cooked, but you can learn a lot from its consistency. Uncooked spaghetti easily breaks in half, but try bundling 25 to 50 pieces of spaghetti and inserting a piece of styrofoam on opposite ends. It should be able to handle a thick book placed on top of the bundle without breaking. Impressive, isn't it? Now, cook it. The form changes completely because pasta absorbs water. It plumps up and, surprisingly, curls despite its straight uncooked form. You can eat it at this point, or follow along and create beautiful artwork.

What You'll Need

Pasta (various shapes and sizes)

Cotton towel

Construction paper or card stock

Dye (optional)

Glue

Boil Your Noodles. Use a variety of shapes like lasagna noodles, ziti, pasta shells, penne, and ribbons. Cook them according to the instructions on the box. Strain, rinse with cold water for ease of handling, and dry them on a cotton towel.

Sketch. Take out a sheet of paper and draw your design, keeping in mind the different noodle shapes you have at your disposal. Will you use different lengths of spaghetti to create a rainbow? How about using ribbons as leaves for a tree? Feel free to cut your noodles to fit your art!

Add a Splash of Color. This is optional, but will definitely help your artwork come to life. Follow the instructions to dye your own pasta, and have fun with colors!

Stick on Your Pasta. Once your pasta is dry and ready, draw with glue where you wish to place your first set of noodles. Don't draw too much at once to make sure you account for the right amount of noodle space. Gently place the noodles on top of the glue lines and softly tap the tops to secure them in place.

Add the Finishing Touches. Continue the process until your artwork is complete, then let dry.

Take It One Step Further

Try three-dimensional noodle art. Use lasagna noodles to make a roadway or cut the ends to make waves in the ocean. And if you're feeling especially musical, use dried pasta inside drums or maracas to make excellent shakers. The sky's the limit!

DIY DYED PASTA

Take a half cup of rubbing alcohol and pour into various bowls of colors you wish to make. Mix them all with about 10 drops of food coloring of your choice. Each bowl should only hold one color. Gently mix in the pasta and stir it well. Remove the pasta and allow it to dry on paper towels for several hours. The colors should deepen as the pasta dries.

TRY IT!

Artwork Digitization

Here's a fun activity that uses technology to preserve art.

Why It Matters

So much can impact how things age. When it comes to art, the right kind of preservation is key to its survival. Chemical reactions can occur due to light exposure that breaks down the pigments and causes discoloration. Temperature fluctuations can cause expanding and contracting. Dirt can affect the exterior of a painting, especially when rubbed in during periodic cleaning. Acidic cleaning agents and continuous vibration have deteriorating effects as well. Learning about the factors that can cause deterioration can aid in preservation efforts.

The Challenge:
Digitize your artwork.

Do Research. For this activity, you'll need to understand basic camera settings.

Aperture determines how much light passes through the lens. This will show how light or dark the image will be.

Shutter speed is the amount of time your subject is exposed to light when taking a photo of it. While a faster shutter speed can prevent blurring when you don't have a steady camera base, a longer shutter speed lets more light in and can result in brighter images.

The ISO refers to the ability to collect light. Before digitalization, ISO referred to the chemical properties of film strips. If it was sensitive, less light was needed. Today, digital sensors take care of this.

Apply Personal Style. There are a few opportunities for this—the artwork and the photo. While you have options on medium and format for your artwork, there are even more ways to preserve art through photography.

Capture your artwork from different angles using the highest resolution available on your camera or smartphone. Usually, these settings are represented in pixels (units of a digital image that make up the larger, complete image). In order to maximize the clarity, density, and color accuracy, you need to maximize the number of pixels.

Wish to document your art over time? Most cameras and phones now have a "slo-mo" and "time-lapse" setting.

Low light conditions? There are multiple flash settings to explore to either add more clarity or additional effects to your photos.

Taking a portrait? Use the portrait mode to blur the foreground or background.

Opt To Print It. You could stop right at taking the perfect photo, or take it to the next level. A color copier or printer will work, but the quality of paper is important. Do you want a glossy or matte finish?

What weight of paper will you use? Consider making more copies.

Display and Protect. Printing your photo still exposes your art to elements that can deteriorate it. Place it inside a clean glass frame away from light, or laminate it (though you may find the finish lacking and invite glare). Be mindful of cleaning agents you use. But more importantly, have fun preserving your masterpiece using modern technology!

Take It One Step Further

Try apps where you can use augmented reality to make a 3D hologram of your work. Other apps will even let you jump inside your painting! Upload your image and put on a virtual reality headset to immerse yourself in a 360-degree view. Tech-ify your artwork!

TRY IT!

Sandcastle Architecture

With simple tools found in your house, you can build an elaborate beach creation on your next weekend getaway!

Why It Matters

Engineering a sandcastle is not an easy task. Using a plastic mold is simple enough, but if you don't know the science behind how to make it sturdy, it could end up in a washout. Using your art skills, sketch a design of what you want it to look like. Will you make a tower with several buckets? What shapes do you envision? What tools will you use to sculpt it? Then put that maker mindset to work! Think about the scientific properties of sand. What makes it stick together? How much water do you need? Engineer a sandcastle that will outlast the next tide!

ASSEMBLE YOUR TOOL KIT.

Mark Mason of Team Sandtastic, the winner of the World Championship Sand Sculpting Competition in British Columbia, Canada, says the basics are simple: Bring two five-gallon buckets, one with the bottom cut out. The bottomless bucket is for building towers; the other will be for transporting water to help you pack down the sand. Bring one shovel for every two to three people on your castle construction crew.

For fine detail carvings, bring along trowels, spatulas, and melon ballers, which can help you remove precise amounts of sand from the sculpture. Also, bring along paintbrushes and straws; they'll let you wipe or blow away loose sand from your carvings without damaging the work of art itself.

FIND YOUR IDEAL LOCATION.

In the world of sand sculpting, not all sand is created equal. Mason tells PM that great sand sculpting requires highly compacted sand. "Building

with coarse sand is like packing marbles. It's only going to pack together at one point," he says. Fine-grain sand is the way to go. Mason says there's a simple way to tell what you're working with: "If you can bike on the beach, it is a good sand sculpting beach."

Not all is lost, though, if the bike test says you're on a less-than-perfect sandcastle-building beach. No matter where you build your sandcastle, the best results come from using plenty of water and compressing the sand with your shovels, feet, and hands as much as possible. Once you've found the beach, make sure to pick the right location on it—preferably, close to the waterline. The perfect spot is just above the high-tide line, where your architectural creation will be protected from tidal destruction and you'll be close enough to the water that you won't wear yourself out.

BUILD A BASE.

Just like solid houses, solid sand

sculptures need strong foundations. To build a base, alternate between piling sand up with your shovel, saturating it with water, and compressing it with your feet and shovel. The more compacted and larger your foundation is, the easier it will be to carve elaborate forms.

Every good castle needs a tower, and that's where your bottomless bucket comes in. "Flip the cut-out bucket on the pile and fill it up, compressing the sand [with your hands] as you go," Mason says. "Do it in thirds. And once you pull the bucket off you'll have a great circular pack of sand."

CARVE YOUR VISION.

Now that the blocks and cylinders of sand are in place, it's sculpting time. Keep it classic with a fortress with spires, or venture beyond castles into the more artistic and unusual side of sand sculpting. No matter which design you pick, Mason's basics should give you a solid foundation from which to work.

Greg LeBon, a member of the seven-time U.S. Open Sandcastle Competition champion team, Archisand, recommends you start carving details from the top down. "The excess sand won't be thrown down on the lower carvings," he says. Once you start in on the detail carving, Mason says to use the straw you brought along in your toolkit. "Some people like to bring a straw so you can carve fine details and blow them out rather than using tools to take them out," he says.

DEFEND YOUR CASTLE.
Finally, there's the big sandcastle debate: moat or no moat? If you've built your castle close to the high-tide mark, then it shouldn't be hard to build one, just dig down into the sand until the water pools up. But the experts warned us that moats are tricky. "If you actually put water in the moat, it has a tendency to erode the sand and cause an early collapse," LeBon says.

If you are pro-moat but want your castle to stand as long as possible, LeBon has a suggestion: simply sculpt the moat. Dig a dry moat and carve in lines to add the appearance of water; when you're done, you've got a defensive barrier that won't undermine your structural integrity.

TRY IT!
Empire Planning

Can you create a world that'll stand the test of time? Find out what it takes to be a superpower!

Why It Matters

People have basic needs like food, water, clothing, and shelter to survive. But, to become a nation considered as a superpower, there are a lot of other factors that play an important role, such as technological and military advancements, agriculture, economics, and human social conditions. Communication, politics, language, and social hierarchy are also essential, because many strong superpowers often assimilate weaker ones into their cultures. We see this repeatedly throughout history, especially after world wars. Using math and technology through computer simulations, science is getting close to being able to predict the rise and fall of superpowers. Do you have what it takes to go up against a computer? Let's see.

The Challenge:

Design an empire that will not just survive, but thrive.

1. Do Your Research. Think about what tools you need to make a superpower. Organize your thoughts and jot down ideas. Answer the following questions:

Are you protected from invasions? Can you withstand a war?

What kind of military and technological advancements do you have to provide an advantage in war and politics?

Does your geography allow for success based on agriculture? Are you self-sustaining? Are you protected from natural disasters? Can you use geography for war tactics?

Does your culture, religions, and ethnicities bring unity to your country? Is everyone able to equally contribute and be productive members of society?

2. Build Your World. In a journal, describe how you see each area being run. Divide them by categories—economics, war tactics, resources and tools, religions, cultures, finances, geography, agriculture, technology, etc. What will make them thrive independently of each other, and collectively?

3. Test Your Theory. Ask a friend to complete this same activity. Exchange your work and note strengths and weaknesses about their ideas. Then share this with an adult mediator or judge.

4. Have Open Discussion. Which superpower is stronger and why? What ideas do you feel strongly about, and which ones would you be open to changing? Rework your original plans to make your empire stronger.

5. Share It. Create a name for your superpower. Identify what makes it unique to other nations and be clear with its strengths. Knowing what you know now, can you predict the rise and fall of current nations around the world? Who knows—you may just be predicting the future!

TIP

Use the engineering design process (page 9) to guide your work.

What You'll Need

Paper

Colored pencils

MAKE IT!
Onager Catapult

Now that you've learned a little bit about building an empire, let's learn about the onager, a weapon used by ancient Romans.

Why It Matters

Building this catapult takes math, science, and engineering skills. Precise measurements are key to making all the pieces work well together. Let's understand the science behind the mechanical energy stored by twisting the torsion spring. Now put that maker grit to work!

What You'll Need

18 No. 6 wood screws, 1½ inches long

1 No. 10 bolt, ¾ inches, with nut and lock washer

36-inch length of 18-pound nylon cord

2 washers, (¾-inch, ¾-inch outside diameter, ¼-inch inside diameter)

2 wooden dowels (⅝-inch-diameter, 1½ inches long)

1 wooden dowel (⅛-inch-diameter, 1½ inches long)

1 small eyebolt and anchor

Power drill with ¹⁄₁₆-, ⅛-, and ¼-inch bits

Yellow wood glue

Manual saw and miter box

Ball-peen hammer

Make the Catapult Frame

1. Drill four $^1/_{16}$-inch pilot holes through the 10-inch frame pieces, with the holes 1¾ inches from each of the four ends and centered vertically.

2. Drill a pilot hole into the center of each end of the crossmembers.

3. Apply glue to the ends of one crossmember and near the pilot holes on the inside of the 10-inch frame pieces; screw the crossmember into place. Repeat this step on the other end.

4. Drill ³⁄₁₆- and ¼-inch holes through the sides of the frame, 5 inches and 5½ inches on center, respectively, from the front of the frame.

5. Glue the footings to the bottom of the frame, flush with the sides and 1 inch on center from the ends. Drill pilot holes into the center of the ends of the footings; screw the wheels into place.

Install the Uprights and Upright Supports

6. Using the drill-glue-and-screw process, secure the uprights to the frame. The uprights should be 4¼ inches on center from the end, the screws driven in from beneath the frame.

7. Drill, glue, and screw a crossbeam flush with the tops of the uprights.

CONTINUED ON NEXT PAGE!

Onager Catapult

8. Drill, glue, and screw the supports into position.

Make the Throwing Arm

9. Drill a ⅛-inch hole through the center of the long dowel about ¾ inch from the end.

10. Use the round face of the hammer to shape the washer into a cup.

11. Attach the washer to the dowel (the cup's rim faces up) using the bolt, lock washer, and nut.

Assemble the Torsion Spring

12. Fold the nylon cord in half twice; tie the loose ends with a square knot.

13. Feed the folded cord through the ¼-inch holes, leaving ½ inch of cord on the outside of the frame. Place a washer over each bundle of cord.

14. Insert the ⅝-inch dowels into the cord loops; position the throwing arm in the middle of the cord.

15. Rotate the dowels toward the front of the frame until the arm presses against the crossbeam. Insert

the ⅛-inch dowel into the smaller hole.

16. Lower the throwing arm down to the frame. Mark spots on the frame and arm where the anchor and eyebolt will be screwed in.

17. Increase the cord's tension by turning the dowels forward. Lower the arm, hook it into position, and remove the locks.

18. To fire the catapult, load the bucket with a projectile and carefully push the anchor hook out of the eyebolt.

Take It One Step Further

This catapult is on wheels. Calculate the distance versus speed while moving it to achieve the trajectory you desire. For example, if you are under attack, do you move your catapult backward as the enemy draws closer? Do you angle it to force your projectiles toward a specific target? Do you launch while moving? How does that affect the trajectory of the projectiles? Have fun experimenting!

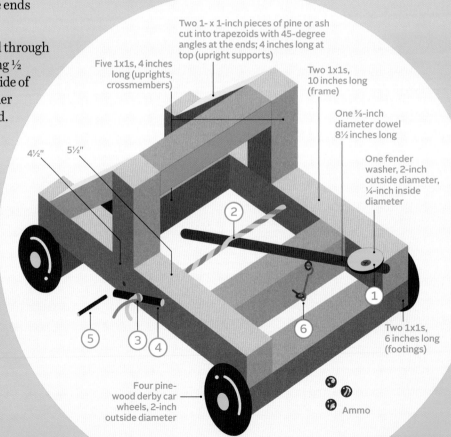

Two 1- x 1-inch pieces of pine or ash cut into trapezoids with 45-degree angles at the ends; 4 inches long at top (upright supports)

Five 1x1s, 4 inches long (uprights, crossmembers)

Two 1x1s, 10 inches long (frame)

One ⅝-inch diameter dowel 8½ inches long

One fender washer, 2-inch outside diameter, ¼-inch inside diameter

4½"

5½"

Two 1x1s, 6 inches long (footings)

Four pinewood derby car wheels, 2-inch outside diameter

Ammo

MAKE IT!
Basketball Catapult

Now, let's modernize the onager catapult to make a game of one-on-one that never has to break for bad weather.

Why It Matters

Jumping in the air to shoot a basketball through a hoop can be fun. Can you change the game by making a basketball catapult? You could launch the ball into a hoop and remove the physical shooter. Now that's a challenge! Let's try it. All it takes is some engineering, math, and science. Why do you need the combination of those three STEAM elements? Think about this. You will need to engineer a court, use math to measure the needed dimensions, and science (physics) to figure out the aerodynamics and trajectory of the ball.

What You'll Need

- 1- x 6- x 12-inch white pine board
- ⅜- x 48-inch round wood dowel
- Wire coat hanger
- 2¾-inch pan-head wood screws
- Optix 0.08 x 8 x 10-inch clear acrylic sheet
- Nerf Rival refill-pack foam balls
- 10 golf tees (two colors)

- Sandpaper
- Miter saw
- Hand miter
- Drill
- ⅜", ³⁄₁₆", ¹⁄₁₆", ¼" twist drill bits
- ¾" spade bit
- Jigsaw
- Wire-cutting pliers
- Tape measure
- Wood glue
- Pencil
- Marker

1. Use a miter saw to cut the 1 x 6 x 12 into lengths of 4½ inches, 4 inches, and 1½ inches. Knock off any rough edges with sandpaper.

2. The 4½-inch section forms the base. Two inches in from one of the cut sides, drill a ⅜-inch hold on center to hold the post. Use a tape measure and a pencil to lightly draw two parallel lines one inch in from the finished sides. Starting ½ inch from the front of the base, mark off five ½-inch increments on each line for the scoring tees. Drill holes at those marks with a ³⁄₁₆-inch bit, then erase the line.

3. The 4-inch section will be the backboard. On one of the cut edges, drill a hole on center with a ⅜-inch bit for the post.

On the face of the backboard, measure up ½ inch from the bottom and drill two holes, 1 inch apart and centered over the post, with a ¹⁄₁₆-inch bit.

4. Use a hand miter saw to cut the dowel to length (see diagram on next page). Spread some glue on its ends and insert one end in the base and the other in the backboard. Align the backboard so its face is parallel with the front edge of the base.

5. Cut a piece of wire coat hanger to about 5 inches using a pair of wire-cutting pliers. Bend the wire so it forms a circle. Grip each end with pliers to make a 90-degree bend. Insert the ends into the holes you drilled in the backboard.

CONTINUED ON NEXT PAGE!

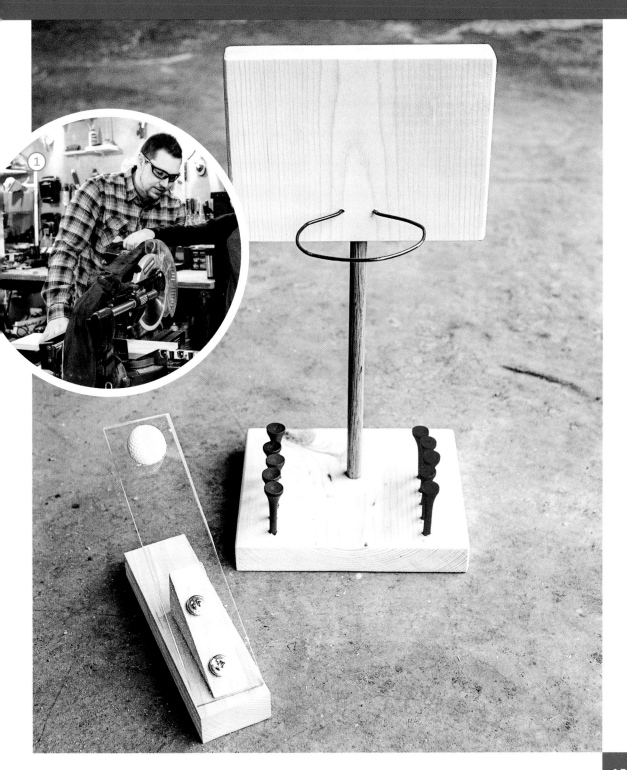

Basketball Catapult

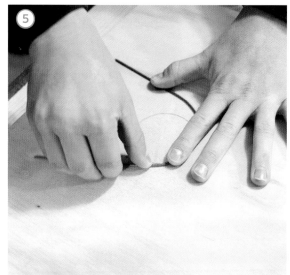

6. Use a marker to indicate the cut line on the acrylic sheet (see diagram), and cut the catapult arm to size using a jigsaw and a fine-cutting blade.

7. Mark the location of the basketball holder on the acrylic according to the diagram, then bore the hole using a ¾-inch spade bit. Drill slowly to

avoid cracking the plastic. Use a ¼-inch twist drill bit to bore the pilot holes for the mounting screws through the other end of the acrylic and into the wedge.

8. The remaining scrap of pine will form the wedge. With one corner as your starting point,

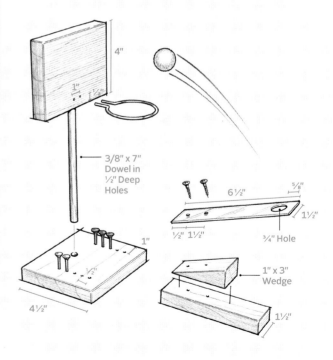

4"

1"
1½"

3/8" x 7"
Dowel in
½" Deep
Holes

6½"
5/8"
1½"
½" 1½"
¾" Hole

1"

1" x 3"
Wedge

1½"

4½"

measure one inch along one side and 3 inches along the other. Mark both points and cut a straight line between them with the jigsaw. Apply a drop of glue to the wedge's back and glue it to the 1½-inch block from step 1. Fasten the catapult to the wedge with two screws.

Plastic Slowdown

Plastic has a smooth surface that reduces friction and allows you to guide smoothly. Garbage bags are shorter, but could work nicely as well. Tarps are usually more texturized and will increase friction.

TIP

If you have a constant stream of water, consider using cylinder-shaped foam or pool noodles to wrap around the edges of your plastic sheet to avoid water runoff on the sides.

MAKE IT!

Backyard Slip n Slide

With a little math, science, and engineering, your backyard slip n slide will be the talk of the neighborhood!

Why It Matters

Ever wondered what goes into creating those fun water slides at amusement parks? At the core, gravity, momentum, and friction are all taken into account to make a fun, smooth—and safe—ride. Engineer your own and invite your friends over!

What You'll Need

8- x 50-feet plastic sheeting

Landscape pins or tent pegs

Garden hose

Liquid soap (We recommend a tear-free bubble bath soap.)

Cylinder-shaped foam or pool noodle (optional)

1. Scout Your Location. You need a steep hill to start from so when gravity takes over, along with the force of a good push to build momentum, you will increase your speed.

2. Think About Your Materials. We recommended an 8- by 50-feet plastic sheeting. While going wider and longer will allow for a longer ride, a shorter piece will help you put your feet down sooner to increase friction and resistance to stop in time if there's an obstacle at the base of your hill.

3. Pin Your Slide Down. Keep your plastic sheeting from moving around with landscape pins or tent pegs. Make sure they are covered with the plastic or some duct tape to avoid injury.

4. Lubricate. Adding water will decrease resistance between your body and the plastic sheet. Make sure you wet the entire slip n slide with water first, especially if you are unable to keep a continuous flow of water.

5. Add Liquid Soap. This helps give you a smoother ride. You will need to add more about every 20 minutes.

6. Have Fun! Test out different ways of sliding and compete with friends to see who can go the longest distance. Will you slide down on your bottom, belly, or your feet? Are you brave enough to go backwards? Enjoy your creation, but be safe!

TIP

If you find yourself on uneven ground and need a smoother ride, try pinning down thick foam sheets underneath the plastic sheeting to avoid any bumps or bruises.

Sand Pendulum

Here's a fun way to learn the basics of frequencies and the mathematical concept of Lissajous figures.

Why It Matters

Some artists throw darts at paint-filled balloons at different intervals to create unique art. Others use a pendulum. With a little math and science, you can too! Lissajous figures are patterns that result when different frequencies (or wavelengths) are applied to the same object. In this case, our object is a soda bottle that drops a line of sand as it swings in two directions at the same time. When the bottle-pendulum is suspended by a single string [Fig. A], it travels the same distance side to side as it does forward and backward. As the pendulum slowly loses energy, the sand trail spirals inward in a circular or elliptical pattern. But if you hang the pendulum by two strings [Fig. B], it moves more quickly in one direction than the other. The lengths of the strings determine the patterns created. To change the patterns, all you have to do is change the length of your strings.

What You'll Need

1 20-oz plastic bottle

String

Construction paper

Masking tape

2 pounds sand

Scissors or utility knife

Cordless drill

1. Cut off the bottom of the plastic bottle with scissors or a utility knife. Drill three holes around the bottom of the bottle, and one in the bottle cap.

2. Tie a 6-inch piece of string in each perimeter hole. Tie those strings to the main pendulum string with square knots. Cut the main string long enough to allow the bottle to hang one to two inches above the ground.

HOW TO USE

Cover the ground with a large piece of construction paper to make it easy to see your creation. Mount the end of the pendulum string to something sturdy above the paper. (We used small screw hooks in the ceiling. Ask your parents first!) Put a piece of masking tape over the hole in the cap, then fill most of the bottle with sand. Remove the tape and quickly put your finger over the hole. Hold the bottle near the edge of the paper, then push it in a circular direction as you let go and remove your finger from the cap. To introduce the second axis, mount a second piece of string at two points in the ceiling so it forms a hanging U. Tie the main pendulum string to the midpoint of this string, fill your bottle with more sand, and try again. How did the shape change? What happens if you change the speed of the pendulum or the length of one of the strings?

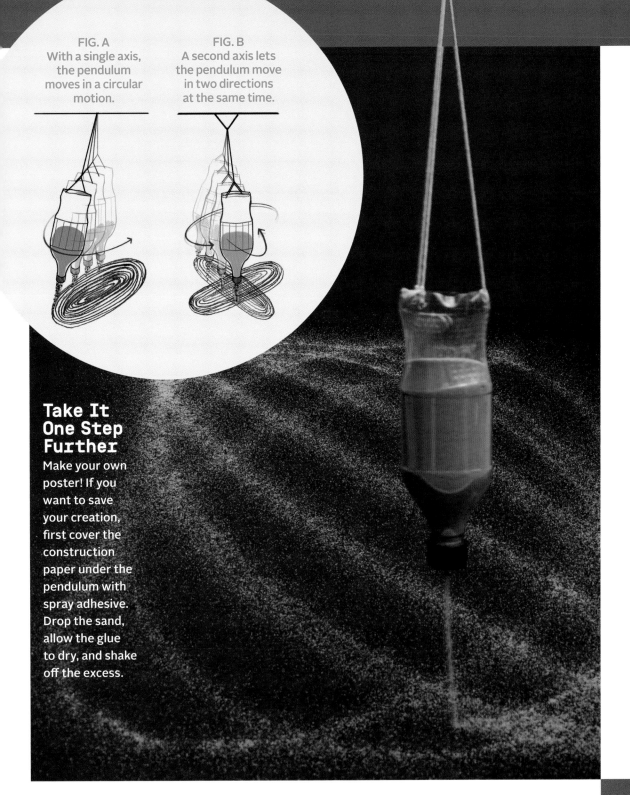

FIG. A
With a single axis, the pendulum moves in a circular motion.

FIG. B
A second axis lets the pendulum move in two directions at the same time.

Take It One Step Further

Make your own poster! If you want to save your creation, first cover the construction paper under the pendulum with spray adhesive. Drop the sand, allow the glue to dry, and shake off the excess.

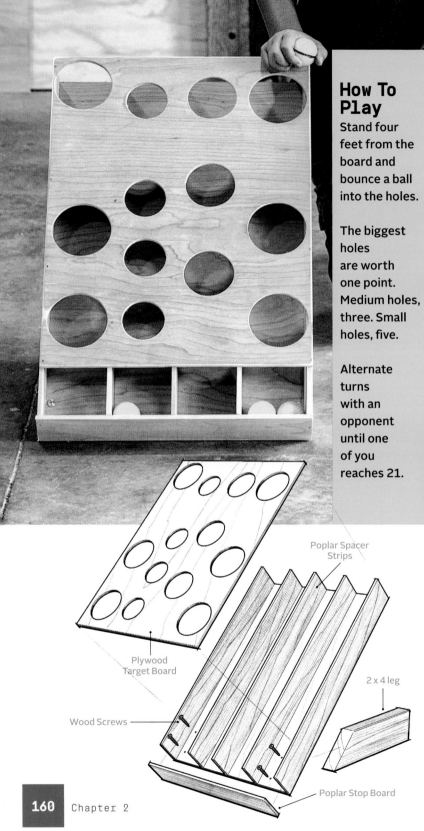

How To Play

Stand four feet from the board and bounce a ball into the holes.

The biggest holes are worth one point. Medium holes, three. Small holes, five.

Alternate turns with an opponent until one of you reaches 21.

Poplar Spacer Strips

Plywood Target Board

Wood Screws

2 x 4 leg

Poplar Stop Board

MAKE IT!
<u>Ball Toss</u>

Bean bag toss or cornhole are fun at family picnics, but can we find a new twist to make it even more exciting?

Why It Matters

To make a ball toss, you will need to apply some basic woodworking techniques, drafting methods, and basic math to design a new game. Understanding the force of gravity, based on the weight of the balls and the materials from which they are made, will be essential in outperforming your opponents.

What You'll Need

4 round-head wood screws (1 inch)

1 quarter sheet 5.2mm lauan plywood (approximately ¼ inch)

6 poplar boards (¼-inch x 3-inch x 2-foot)

1 piece of 2 x 4 scrap, at least 30 inches long

6 balls (1½-inch tennis, practice golf, or Nerf-gun balls)

Table saw and 80-tpi blade

Miter saw

Drill

Holesaw bits (2-, 2½-, and 3-inch)

Wood glue

Tape measure

Rafter square

1. Use a table saw with an 80-tpi blade to rip the plywood to 16 inches wide, then crosscut it into two pieces. One piece, the target board, should be 21 inches long. The other, the base, should be 24 inches.

2. Cut five 24-inch-long spacer strips from the ¼-inch poplar boards with a miter saw. Crosscut one piece of poplar to 16 inches to create the stop board at the bottom of the game.

3. Mark the spacer-strip locations on the target board and the base using a pencil, tape measure, and rafter square [Fig. A]. The space between each strip should be about 3 11/16 inches, but there's no need to get fussy about placement. As long as you mark both boards with identical spacing, everything will line up.

4. Clamp the target board to a piece of scrap wood for a cleaner cut. Use a drill and the holesaw to bore holes in the target board [Fig. B]. Use the same holesaw for each vertical segment of the board, making sure the holes are centered between the lines. Glue the spacer strips to the target board and let the glue dry for an hour

5. Apply a band of glue on top of each spacer strip [Fig. C] and press the backboard into position. Place a weighted object on the board to hold it down while the glue dries.

6. Glue the stop board to the bottom of the spacer strips and let the glue dry for 15 minutes.

7. Use a miter saw to crosscut two 2 x 4 boards to 15 inches, then to cut a 56-degree angle on the end of each piece to create the legs.

8. Attach the game board to the legs with the round-head wood screws [Fig. D].

MAKE IT!

Matchbox Car Belt

Bring your favorite toy around without having to deal with bulky pockets!

Why It Matters

Velcro has the perfect adhesive properties to easily remove the toy car from your belt when it's time to play and then put it back in place for a fashion statement—and ease of transport! The elasticity of the bicycle tire makes designing a belt feel like it was engineered just for you. Practice your math skills to measure holes for a perfect fit!

What You'll Need

1 bicycle road tire (26-inch)

1 metal buckle back (1¾-inch)

1 aluminum binding post (³⁄₁₆- x ¼-inch)

1 toy car (like Matchbox)

1 Industrial-strength 2- x 4-inch Velcro (model 90199)

1. Use heavy-duty kitchen shears to cut the tire across the tread. Next, evenly cut along both sides of the tread down the length of the tire to produce the 1¼-inch belt width. (You may want to test the width on a favorite pair of jeans to confirm the fit.)

2. Clamp the buckle back to a workbench and enlarge the buckle's mounting hole with a ¹³⁄₆₄-inch twist drill bit and a cordless drill. The binding-post base should slide neatly into the hole when you're done.

3. Drill a matching ¹³⁄₆₄-inch hole in the center of the belt, ½ inch from an end.

4. Position the buckle back behind the belt, and thread the binding-post screw through the hole in the belt and into the post. Tighten the screw with a straight blade screwdriver. The screw head should pinch slightly into the belt.

5. With the kid wearing the belt around his or her waist, have an adult mark the belt's length. Cut the belt to a length that allows the buckle's hook to overlap the belt's end by ½ inch.

6. Drill a centered ⁵⁄₃₂-inch hole a half inch from the end of the belt that doesn't have the buckle.

7. Cut a strip of the soft and fuzzy side of the Velcro and attach it to the buckle. Trim off the excess.

8. Cut a matching piece of Velcro to ½- by 2-inches, and stick it on the bottom of the car. Stick the car to the belt.

Bike Tire

Binding Post

Metal Buckle Back

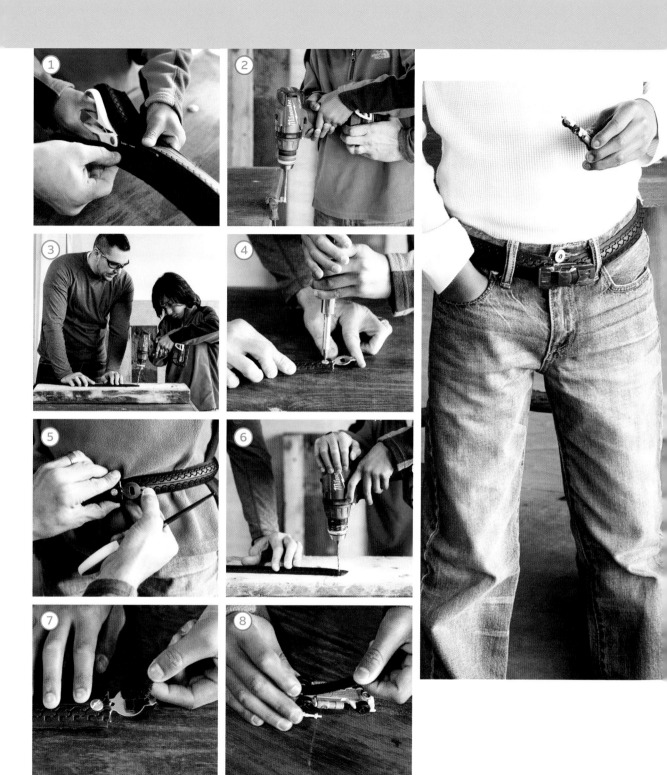

TIP

If you live in Alaska—or even northern Minnesota—you might want to use standard batteries during the winter.

Solar-Powered Night-Light

Never worry about whether or not you have batteries on hand again!

Why It Matters

A solar-powered night-light may sound counterintuitive, but when the night-light isn't in use during the day, it captures ambient light. Just leave it near a window and open the blinds. By capturing natural or artificial light, you can use the technology and science of a circuitry paired with a solar cell to power up a light that will stay lit throughout the night. The two AA batteries hold enough power to keep the night-light running until the sun comes up, then the solar panel starts collecting again and the process begins all over.

What You'll Need

1 action figure with open-grasp hand

26 inches 22-AWG wire

1 1N914 diode 1 small solar panel, 3.0-volt 70-milliamp with wires

2 AA rechargeable batteries

1 LED lamp (10-millimeter) (RadioShack item No. 2760006)

1 AA battery holder (RadioShack item No. 2700408)

1 toggle switch

20 1-inch 16-gauge finishing nails

1 No. 8 1-inch sheet metal screw

¼- x 4- x 24-inch poplar board

½- x 3- x 24-inch poplar board

Multipurpose adhesive

Soldering gun or crimp connectors

1. Crosscut the top panel from the 4-inch poplar board. A 3½-inch piece should accommodate most action figures.

2. Using twist-drill bits and a cordless drill, make a ³⁄₁₆-inch hole for the LED wire and a ½-inch hole for the switch. Use a spade bit to make the ¾-inch hole for the leads from the solar panel.

3. Crosscut the box ends and sides from the 3-inch poplar to accommodate the top panel. Use wood glue and finish nails to fasten the parts, and a nail set to countersink the nailheads.

4. Cut two 10-inch pieces of wire. Use wire strippers to remove ³⁄₈ inch of insulation from all four ends. Take one end of each wire and solder it to the LED. Wrap connections with electrical tape. Twist these wires together and poke them down through the hole in the box cover.

5. Take the remaining 6-inch piece of wire and strip ¼ inch off each end. Poke one end through a hole in a switch terminal and solder. Beneath the box top, attach the positive wire from the LED to the other terminal on the switch.

6. Feed the switch leads down through the box and hold the switch in place by tightening the nut from below. Drop the leads from the solar panel down into the box and glue the panel in place.

CONTINUED ON NEXT PAGE!

Solar-Powered Night-light

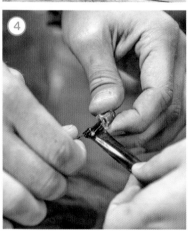

7. Use the schematic above to make the remaining connections. First, solder together the free LED wire and the negative wires from the solar cell and battery pack. On the other side of the solar cell, solder the positive wire to the diode. Diodes are directional, so make sure that the black band on the diode is on the side of the circuit nearer the battery holder. Solder the other side of the diode to the free wire on the switch and the positive wire from the battery.

8. Place two batteries in the holder and test the circuit. If it works, glue the holder to the inside of the box wall. If not, double-check the wiring against the schematic and be sure that you have the batteries in the holder correctly.

9. Attach the action figure by boring a pilot hole from the inside of the box using a $\frac{3}{32}$-inch bit. Use the same bit to make a hole in the foot of the action figure. Mount the action figure on the box by driving the sheet-metal screw through the box and into the figure's foot, and place the LED in its hand.

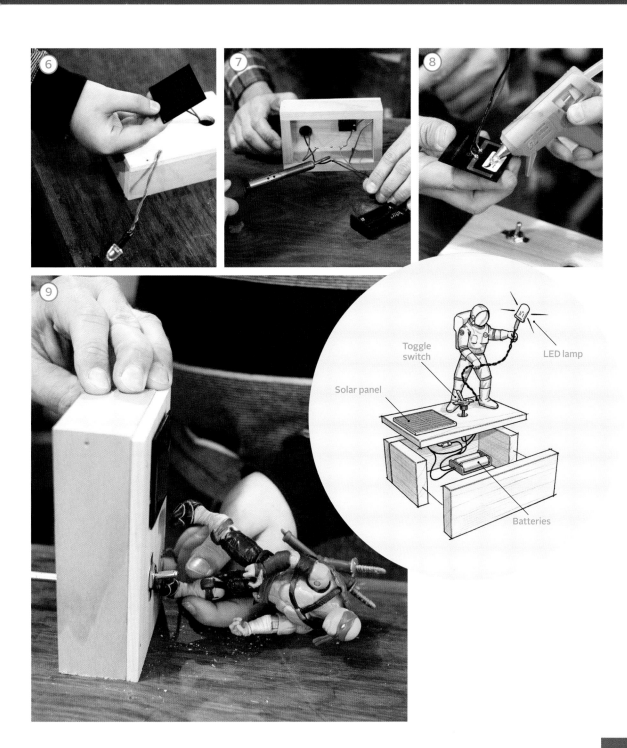

Toggle switch

Solar panel

LED lamp

Batteries

MAKE IT!

Time Capsule

They say you learn a lot from studying history, so preserve yours and see if you learn something new about yourself when you open this time capsule in the future.

Why It Matters

Lock away a specific time in your history, and relive it down the road. Will you reference one of NASA's rovers landing on Mars? Will you share what it was like to live through COVID-19? How about making a prediction for the future and seeing if it comes true? The possibilities are endless! Use your engineering skills to give your time capsule an airtight seal, then add some artistic flair with decorations that reflect the year you buried it.

FUN FACT

A time capsule dating back to 1795 was supposedly placed by Sam Adams and Paul Revere. In it was a Massachusetts state seal, a series of coins from the era, front pages of five newspapers, and a silver marker for the box.

What You'll Need

1 PVC pipe (3½-inch-diameter)

1 container each PVC primer and cement

1 PVC end cap (3½-inch)

1 PVC test plug (3½-inch)

1 can spray paint

Hammer

1. Measure and mark off with a felt-tipped pen the length of the pipe necessary to hold your contents. We chose 14½ inches.

2. If the child is at least 12 years old and has some experience, with careful adult supervision they can use a miter saw to crosscut the pipe. If not, a standard eight-point carpentry handsaw is a safe alternative.

3. Apply PVC primer to the end of the pipe and on the inside of the end cap. (Be sure to open the windows for ventilation.)

4. Using the applicator tool, spread a thick layer of PVC cement onto the end of the pipe, and a thin layer on the inside of the end cap.

5. With the PVC pipe upright, tap the end cap on with a dead-blow hammer or mallet. Twist the end cap slightly to evenly distribute the cement, then finish tapping the cap until it is firmly seated.

6. Fill the time capsule with whatever you like, preferably nonperishable items. Be sure to include something that indicates the date of the contents.

7. Insert the test plug into the pipe and wind the wing nut until it is firmly tightened.

8. Spray-paint the capsule.

Test Plug — 3½" — 14½" — End Cap

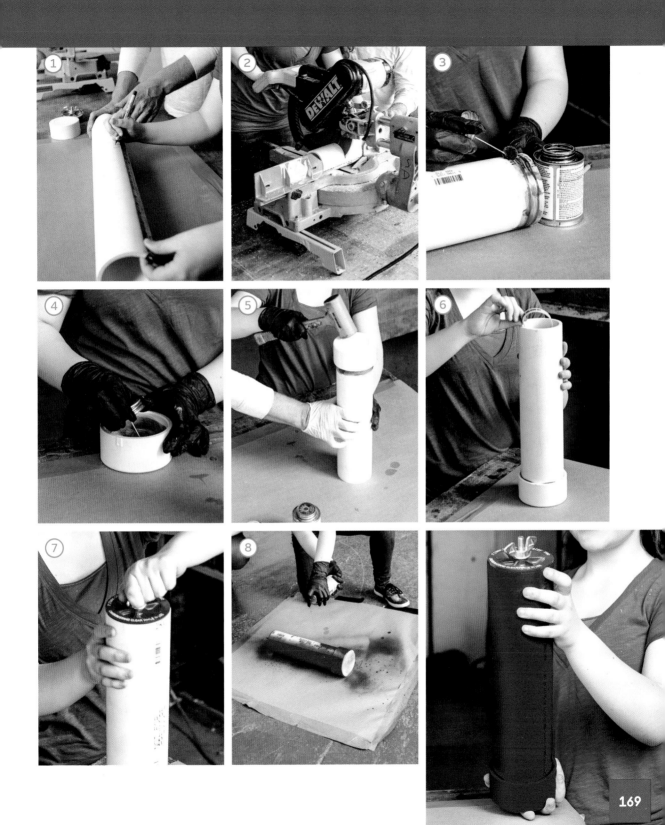

MAKE IT!
Periscope

Nothing wrong with being a little ~~nosy~~ curious. In fact, the most curious people end up making the best discoveries. Gear up properly with this project!

Why It Matters

Becoming an international spy takes a lot of smarts. This activity will teach you how prisms work, building on what you learned about refraction with Jell-O in Chapter 1 (page 12). Blend in some engineering and math to angle your mirrors properly for a periscope you can use at your next secret spy mission!

What You'll Need

Two pieces 3- x 15-inch foam board

Two pieces 3½- x 18-inch foam board

Two pieces 3- x 3-inch foam board

Two 3- x 3-inch mirrors

Duct tape

How It Works

To understand the optics of periscopes, think of the letter Z. The light reflected from an object hits a mirror tilted at 45 degrees at the top of the device. The light then bounces to an identically angled mirror at the bottom, providing the image we see when we look into a periscope. If you follow the path of light, it's approximately Z-shaped.

1. Cut foam board to size.

2. Assemble a four-sided chamber by alternating the placement of the 3- x 15-inch and 3½- x 18-inch pieces and securing them with tape; there should be 3-inch-square openings at the top front and lower back of the chamber.

3. Cap both ends by taping 3- x 3-inch foam-board pieces into place.

4. Fold two 3-inch-long strips of tape at a right angle, and stick them to two opposite edges of each mirror.

5. Fasten the mirrors inside the chamber. To get the 45-degree angle, position the mirrors so that their front edges align with those of the top and bottom openings; when viewed head-on, the mirrors should fill the 3-inch openings.

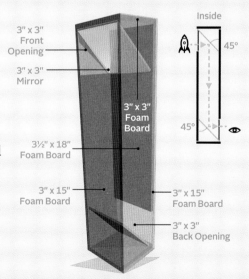

3" x 3" Front Opening

3" x 3" Mirror

3" x 3" Foam Board

3½" x 18" Foam Board

3" x 15" Foam Board

Inside

45°

45°

3" x 15" Foam Board

3" x 3" Back Opening

MAKE IT!
Pipe Chime

A simple assemblage of pipe, twine, screws, and lumber uses ancient Greek geometry and the pentatonic scale to coax a sweet song from a gentle breeze.

Why It Matters

What makes this instrument unique is that it produces sound based on many of the STEAM elements. When the hollow metal pipes are struck, they will vibrate based on some math (geometry for shape and length of the bar) and physics (acceleration due to gravity), as well as the science of how air currents may affect movement and sound. Be sure to place your chime where there's sure to be a breeze!

What You'll Need

- 1 x 6 lumber
- 7 eye screws
- 5 feet of Type M ¾-inch copper tubing
- 5 No. 6 1-inch machine screws and nuts
- Nylon twine
- Glue

Map Pipe Mounts. Center a 4½-inch-diameter circle in a 5½-inch-square cut of lumber. Mark the circle at five equidistant points. Insert eye screws at the circle's center and at all five points.

Cue Pythagoras. Cut five pieces of tubing to the lengths in the table below and deburr. The chime's five notes, which correspond to a piano's black keys, make up the minor pentatonic scale. The notes are pleasing in any order. The ancient Greeks, such as Pythagoras, were the first to study the link between the length of a vibrating body and the notes of a musical scale.

Tie With Twine. Drill a $\frac{5}{32}$-inch hole through each pipe as listed in the table. These hanging points produce the best chime resonance. Insert a machine screw through the hole and fit a nut onto the screw shank. Tie a 7-inch length of twine from the circle of eye screws to the screw shank in each pipe.

Hang The Chime. Use a 2½-inch holesaw to cut a clapper from a 1x scrap. Use more 1x waste to make a V-shaped, 3-inch-long wind scoop. Hang each from the center eye screw. Cut and glue two smaller 1x squares to the top of the first square. Top-center-mount an eye screw in the smallest square. Hang the chime in the breeze and enjoy.

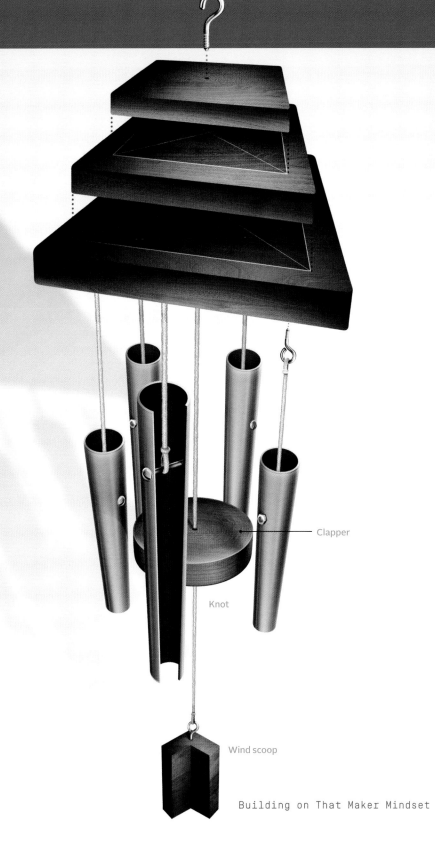

Clapper

Knot

Wind scoop

Building on That Maker Mindset

MAKE IT!

Boot-Box Boombox

Blend old-school electronics skills and smartphone tech to create a musical blast from the past!

Why It Matters

Who doesn't love music? You listen to it at parties, dances, and on road trips. Using technology and science, you can engineer a device to play your music! First, you might want to do a little research to brush up on your circuitry knowledge. Then get to work! Don't forget to employ some art skills to design the shape and decorate it. Will you add a handle, carrying case, or secret compartment? What will make your boombox unique? Don't forget the technology! What device will play your music, an MP3 Player, iPod, or phone? How loud will it be? Will you host a neighborhood karaoke night?

What You'll Need

1 Dayton Audio DTA-2 Class T Audio Amplifier Module

9-volt battery clip

12 VDC 2000mA 2A switching power supply, 2.5-mm plug (optional)

8 AA battery holder

8 AA batteries

6 feet 3.5-mm male-to-male stereo cable

2 Dayton Audio DAEX25 Sound Exciters (speakers)

2 ferrite rings, ½-inch diameter

2 ceramic-disc capacitors

Soldering iron

Solder

Hot-glue gun

Boot box

Duct tape

Wire the Amplifier

1. Place the amplifier on a work surface, flat side down; position the amp so that the row of four small holes is on the top edge.

2. Strip ¼ inch of the ends of the two battery-clip wires; slip the tips of the wires through two of the four holes closer to the amp's right corner, with the black wire in the outermost hole. Bend and then solder the tips to the flat side of the amp.

3. Pair two sets of the red-and-black wires included with the speakers; cut into 15-inch lengths. Strip ¼ inch of each wire tip, then loop each pair once around the rim of a ferrite donut.

4. Wrap a tip of one red and one black wire around the legs of a capacitor. Slip one leg through each of the holes next to those where the battery-clip wires are soldered. The wire colors must alternate: black, red, black, red. Solder the capacitor, legs, and wires, to the amp. (This pair of wires feeds one of the speakers.)

5. Locate the two holes, about ½ inch from the right side of the amp. Repeat Step 4, slipping the tip of a length of black wire through the hole marked with a minus (negative) sign, and a red wire tip through the other hole marked with a plus (positive) sign. Solder in place. (This pair of wires feeds the other speaker.)

CONTINUED ON NEXT PAGE!

Boot-Box Boombox

Attach the Components Inside the Box

6. Apply glue to the flat side of the amp assembly, and stick it to the inside of one of the two larger faces of the boot box. Position the amp so that the switch-ribbon cable reaches the point on the side of the box where you will install the volume-control knob (Step 9).

7. Using the self-adhesive tape on each exciter (speaker), affix them to the same face of the box as the amp. Clip the speakers to the two sets of wires attached to the capacitors.

8. Glue the battery pack near a lower corner inside the box. Attach the battery pack to the amp using the clip.

9. Remove the knob from the volume control (this is also the on/off switch). Poke a hole through a side of the box large enough to fit the stem of the volume control. Place the stem through the hole, reattach the knob, and glue the assembly to the inside of the box.

10. Plug one end of the switch ribbon into the amp and the other end into the volume-control unit. Glue down the ribbon.

11. Plug the ends of the speaker cable into the amp and the device that holds your music library.

Attach Your Device

12. Turn on your device with the volume on high, choose your favorite playlist, and press play. Close the box—and rock on!

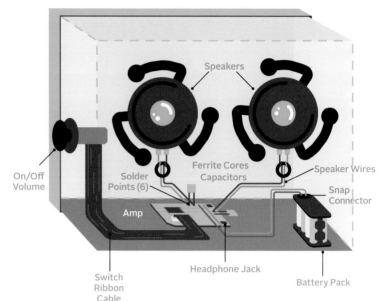

On/Off Volume

Speakers

Ferrite Cores Capacitors

Speaker Wires

Solder Points (6)

Snap Connector

Amp

Switch Ribbon Cable

Headphone Jack

Battery Pack

TIP

Look up amps, conductors, insulators, capacitors, circuits, power supplies, and circuits.

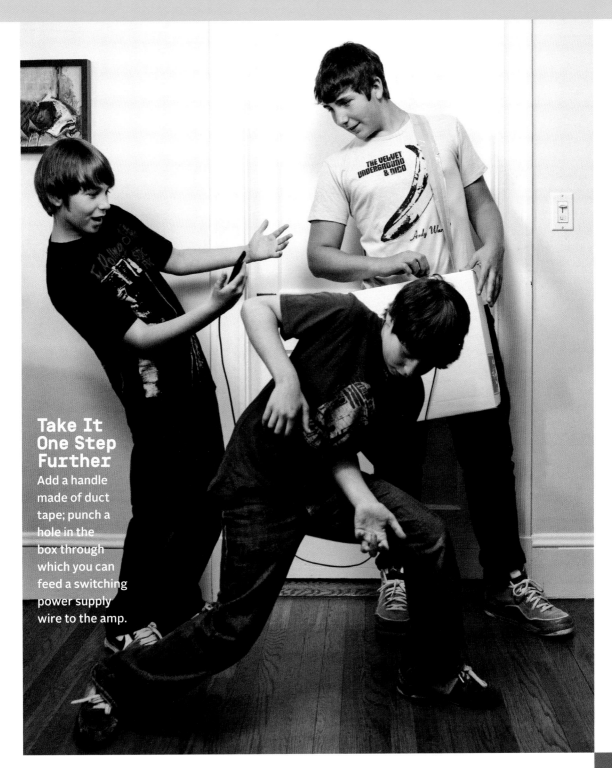

Take It One Step Further

Add a handle made of duct tape; punch a hole in the box through which you can feed a switching power supply wire to the amp.

MAKE IT!

Mars Rover

Dreaming of working for NASA one day? This activity teaches the basics of electrical circuitry, motors, and even lighting to get you started!

Why It Matters

On February 18, 2021, NASA launched its space rover, Perseverance, to touch down on Mars. It will search for signs of life and collect samples from the surface to bring back to Earth for analysis. The scientific data obtained from this mission will contribute immensely to both science and technology fields. While we're waiting on results, let's build a Mars robot rover using engineering, technology, and science skills. Get ready for some robotics and circuitry fun!

What You'll Need

Elenco 2-in-1 Gearbox kit

AA-battery case with switch

3-volt 10-mm LED (one that can handle 3 volts or more)

2 AA batteries

22-gauge multistrand black wire, cut into two 6-inch lengths

22-gauge multistrand red wire, cut into two 6-inch lengths

1 baby bottle cap or other plastic-dome piece (large bottle top, capsule for vending-machine toys)

2 handballs or other hollow, squishy balls (2-inch-diameter)

½-inch-thick foam board, cut into a 2½- x 4½-inch piece

1 wine bottle cork

Aluminum foil, crepe paper, construction paper, gift paper (optional)

Pipe cleaners (optional)

Hot-glue gun

Drill and ⁷⁄₆₄-inch drill bit

Wire cutter/stripper

Ruler

Scissors

Electrical tape

Adhesive tape

Build The Engine

1. Assemble the Elenco 2-in-1 Gearbox by following the instructions included in the kit. For this project, use the longest of the three shafts provided as the front axle and disregard the nylon connectors. The rover's speed is determined by the cogs you choose: Gear ratios of 1:60 and 1:288 are fast and slow, respectively.

2. Strip ¾ inch of insulation from each end of two 6-inch black wires and two 6-inch red wires.

3. Thread the end of a black wire through the hole in one of the motor terminals and secure it by folding the wire back on itself and twisting; repeat the process with red wire at the other terminal.

4. Carefully separate the legs of the LED; they're fragile, so take care not to break them off.

5. Tightly wrap one end of the exposed part of the black wire around the short leg of the LED; do the same with the red wire around the long LED leg.

CONTINUED ON NEXT PAGE!

Mars Rover

6. Strip ½ inch of the battery-case wire ends.

7. Twist together the black wires from the motor, battery case, and LED; repeat with red wires.

8. Wrap all exposed wires tightly with electrical tape, including those around the legs of the LEDs and the terminals on the motor.

9. Put batteries in case; flip switch to test circuit.

Assemble the Craft

1. Drill a ⁷⁄₆₄-inch hole into each ball. Slide the balls onto the axle ends.

2. Decorate the piece of foam by wrapping it in foil, construction paper, or gift paper—go nuts!

3. Use a hot-glue gun to secure the gearbox to the body.

4. On the opposite end, glue on the cork. You may need to cut down the cork to ensure that the body is level. Let the glue dry.

5. Flip over the body and glue the battery pack near one end of the surface; let dry. This is the top of the rover's body.

6. Glue the LED terminals and wires to the top of the rover.

7. Glue the translucent baby bottle cap to the top of the rover, covering the LED. Let dry.

8. Decorate with pipe cleaners, crepe paper, or other gewgaws to make your rover look galactically awesome!

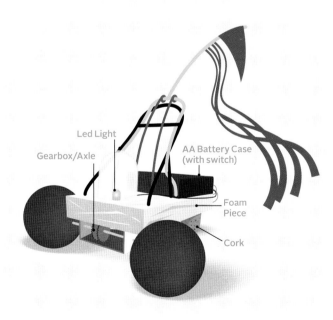

Led Light

Gearbox/Axle

AA Battery Case (with switch)

Foam Piece

Cork

CHAPTER 3

Putting It All Together

Challenge yourself and put that maker mindset to work! Let the engineering design process guide you through the following projects.

MAKE IT!
Electronic Fruit Clock

Yes, fruits are great for getting your vitamins, but did you know they can power up a clock too?

Why It Matters

Using modern technology, engineers and scientists found creative methods to power all different kinds of clocks. Some of the world's most interesting public clocks are a sight to behold with incredible ways of marking time. Japan's water clock, for example, combines water, art, programming, and math to create patterns as water falls in artistic musical note shapes. For this activity, let's try creating a fruit clock by hacking a traditional battery-powered clock without actual batteries. Citrus fruits such as lemons, oranges, limes, and grapefruit work best due to their high level of acidity. You could generate enough power to last several days!

What You'll Need

2 acidic citrus fruits (lemons, oranges, limes, or grapefruit)

1 battery-operated digital clock (like the Dollar Store Kitchen Timer)

2 alligator clips or wires

2 copper plates

2 zinc plates

1. Gather your fruit and play with it a little! Squeeze the fruit or apply pressure around it as you would to playdough for 30 seconds. This mixes up the inside pulp and breaks down the cell walls. Then, put the fruit aside.

2. The wires need to be exposed in order for the metal to serve as a conductor and create a closed circuit. If it is surrounded by plastic tubing (an insulator), the wires will need to be stripped down to expose the metal inside. Or you could attach alligator clips instead of using wires if the alligator clips were purchased with wires already attached. Make sure you have a tight, metal on metal contact. Any space in the circuit will prevent the flow of electrons.

3. Insert one copper plate and one zinc plate into each lemon. Gently push in each plate at least two inches so it's deep enough to conduct electricity without creating any spaces in the circuit.

4. Attach the alligator clips or exposed wires by connecting them to the battery terminal of the clock. You may need to take off the backing of the battery compartment to find the lead wires, which are typically black and red in color. Of course, if there is a battery inserted, that should be removed. The black wire needs to be connected to the zinc plate and the red wire to the copper plate. Simply tie the wire around the hole in the plate or use tape, but make sure to attach it with metal on metal contact in some way. This would prevent the need for alligator clips, which can be used in place of your wires.

5. Enjoy your electronic hack to make a digitized fruit clock!

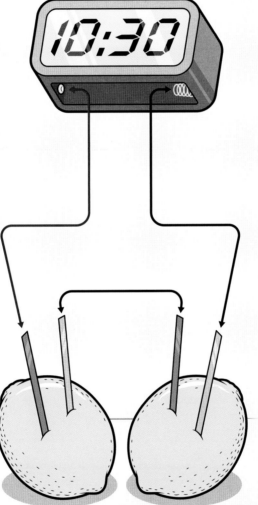

Try experimenting with other materials by switching out citrus fruits or conductive materials. Remember: You are creating a power source (battery) to power up a digitized clock using fruit. That means you need to create a closed circuit to carry the electrons. What else can you engineer with circuits? Use your math skills to set a timer or change the time. Want some cool LED art? Power up each LED with about four lemon batteries! Tip: The zinc end needs to be connected to the negative side and the copper to the positive side in order for it to work. Have fun engineering your electronic hacked fruit clock!

Project Notes

Zinc really wants to push electrons away, while copper draws them in. Citrus juice connects them to allow a chemical reaction to occur. When zinc is exposed to the acid in the juice, the acid oxidizes or removes electrons from the zinc. Remember, the electrons want to get to the copper! The chemical reaction allows the electrons to move to the copper to conduct electricity. The lemon battery power will be weak, but it's enough to power a small clock.

MAKE IT!
Secret Message Transporter Machine

Discover the beauty of inventing!

Why It Matters

Inventions are a product of a maker's hard work and determination, but it doesn't always have to be grand. Building something that has never been done before always starts with a simple idea. Take the Breakfast Machine, for example. Someone built it completely out of Lego pieces to help ease the task of a father who cooks breakfast every Saturday and Sunday—that's 104 days out of the year! With that same maker mindset, we can take what we've learned so far about STEAM to come up with a new machine!

Ideas for What You'll Need

Body: cardboard, paper towel tubes, water bottle, or foam

Wheels: CDs, washers, plastic lids, bottle caps, or cylindrical containers

Axles: straws, wooden skewers, or pencils

Energy Source: balloon

Adhesives: glue, tape, foam, gum, or modeling clay

Tools: scissors, drill, your hands

Let's run through this project using the engineering design process, shall we?

Identify the Problem. Should you want to build your own machine, think about how we live day to day. Is there a difficult chore you wish you could make easier? Maybe a pet feeder or a robot that can take out the trash? Start out small and build on it. For the sake of this project, how about we build a secret message transporter?

Brainstorm Possible Solutions. In order to do that, we need to understand the science behind simple machines or devices with little to no moving parts. Read up on the six types of simple machines: lever, pulley, inclined plane, wedge, screw, and wheel and axle. With a change in direction or amount of force, they can complete any task.

Select the Best Option After Exploring Your Ideas. For this project, consider the body, wheels, and axles of your transporter. The axles connect the wheels to the body and allow for movement. It should make for the perfect simple machine.

Build a Prototype. Gather your materials and get to work.

Make the Transporter.

1. Depending on what you choose for the body, cut or drill holes large enough for your axles to fit through, about an inch in from each end of the body near the center, resulting in a total of four holes. Use your math skills!

2. Cut or drill a small hole into each of your wheels, right in the center to even the distribution of weight.

CONTINUED ON NEXT PAGE!

Secret Message Transporter Machine

TIP

If you notice the axles sliding around a bit, you might need to reduce the length of your axles or use adhesive to secure the axles and keep the wheels from wobbling. If the hole is too large, glue some modeling clay or extra foam on the outside of your wheel where it meets the axles. Do this all the way around. Make sure the wheels can spin freely! A wheel and axle reduce friction, allowing the car or load to roll with an attached energy source.

3. Place your axles through the two holes at each end and attach a wheel on each side. Is it starting to look like a car? Good!

Make Your Transporter Move.

1. Tape a bendy straw to the top of your transporter. Make sure it's in line vertically with the body. The straw should be on the edge of the body where you want to blow in to propel it forward.

2. Use a rubber band to tighten the bendy part of the straw inside the balloon to the outer edge. The balloon will release stored energy and work with your axles to move your machine.

TIP

Be sure to pinch the end of the balloon after you inflate it to angle your transporter. Set it down before releasing the air to keep unnecessary air from escaping and increase the distance it will travel.

Test and Improve Your Prototype.
Run your trials and see if you can make it better.

1. Use your cellphone to take videos of your testing phase. Try using different weights to increase or decrease speed.

2. Build on your design. Get creative and tech-ify it! Will you add a secret compartment so your message is more secure? Maybe a lock instead? Will you attach LEDs to make it easier to use in the dark?

TRY IT!

Camping Setup Like a Pro

There's nothing like camping to find your calm—as long as you're prepared, that is. Let's walk through everything you need to know about setting up camp, from basic Boy Scout knowledge to expert tips that you can use at your next campout.

Why It Matters

This activity is the perfect integration of STEAM. Science comes into play when creating a water filtration system, knowing the degrees to cook your meals, using energy sources, and more. Technology is needed to research a spot online as well as using GPS tracking to find your location. Engineering will be required to set up a tent that can withstand the outdoor elements. Art will be useful in keeping the camp mess-free. Math will help you figure out the distance to the closest water source, bathroom, or store. Let's get outdoors!

Picking the Right Campsite

CAR CAMPERS: **EASE AND COMFORT**

Car camping allows you to forgo hiking to the campsite and just drive there instead. This is faster and allows you to bring a few luxury items along with you.

HIKE-IN CAMPERS: **IT'S ALL ABOUT WATER**

A good rule of thumb: Stay 200 feet away from water to avoid adding any kind of waste to the lake, river, or stream, and also to steer clear of contributing to erosion or bothering wild animals that visit the water.

Don't stray too far, though, because chances are you'll need water for cooking, drinking, and, depending on how far you roam, maybe even bathing. In case you must make several trips to the water source, stay close.

The Bureau of Land Management website is a great option, for instance, as is the U.S. Forest Service. Public lands are beautiful and remote.

Tent 101

HOW TO PICK ONE

Start by considering two factors:

- Number of people sleeping in the tent
- When and where you will be using it

Typically, tents fall into two categories:

- A **three-season tent** is meant to be used from late spring to early fall.
- A **four-season shelter,** as the name implies, is supposed to be robust enough to use during the winter or on mountaineering expeditions at higher altitude.

Unless you need cold-weather performance—or you're an ultralight hiker packing only a super-lightweight shelter—pick a three-season tent. These shelters are the most versatile and comfortable and meet the needs of most campers.

A recommendation: Find a tent that is affordable, durable, weather-resistant, and easy to set up.

CONTINUED ON NEXT PAGE!

Set Up Camp Like a Pro

Other features to bear in mind:

Headroom (especially if you're tall)

Doors! It's a lot easier to sleep in an enclosed space, especially for a few days, if you have multiple ways to get in and out.

Floor space. If you're not worried about weight, then choosing more square footage can provide room for storing extra gear—or simply create a more comfortable environment.

THE PROPER SPOT TO PITCH A TENT
Choose a generally flat spot so you don't end up sliding downhill on your sleeping pad. Check for any hidden tree roots or rocks that'll interfere with a good night's sleep.

After that, keep these three things in mind:

Water: Pick a place with adequate drainage in case rain starts to fall. A good rain fly will help to keep the interior of the tent dry even in a downpour, but if your shelter is set up in the path of flowing water, things can get very wet very quickly.

Sun: In the morning, the sun's rays can quickly heat up the interior of a tent. Pick a spot with some shade. Just be sure no tree branches are likely to come falling down on you in the middle of the night.

Wind: Trees can also serve as a windbreak, as can large rocks or cliff faces. A steady breeze can ruffle the tent all night long, making it hard to sleep. By looking for natural shelters from the elements however, you may get some relief, even when weather conditions are less than ideal.

HOW TO PITCH A TENT
1. Lay the tent on the ground, stretch it out, and then use stakes to secure the corners in place. The vast majority of tents come with built-in loops that are strategically placed along its perimeter.

2. Place stakes inside built-in loops. Pull them tight while the stakes are hammered into the ground.

3. Use the included poles to give the tent its structure. The setup process for each model varies slightly, but usually it involves locking the poles into a series of hooks, tabs, and sleeves to hold them firmly in place. Place poles in designated holes found along the edges of the exterior of the tent, usually on opposite sides from one another (some tents will color-code the tabs and poles to make this process easier). When the poles are bent to fit into place, the tent will rise up and take shape.

The Flame:
HOW TO BUILD A CAMPFIRE
No campsite is complete without a fire. But don't feel nervous or dismayed if you've never built a fire or struggle with feeding the flames. It's easier than you think, as long as you remember the steps.

1. FIND YOUR FIRE PIT.
If you're camping at a designated campsite, you'll probably find a few fire rings already in place.

If not, you'll want to build one by collecting small stones and placing them in a circle on the ground. This prevents the fire from spreading and growing out of control.

Remember: Even with a fire ring in place, it is important to stay vigilant. Stray embers can still start a fire if they are carried by the wind onto dry grass, weeds, or small pieces of wood.

Read the instructions and watch setup videos to save you time and frustration in the backcountry. It can be a real challenge to pitch a tent for the first time in the dark or during a rainstorm when all you really want to do is crawl inside and relax.

Before setting out for the backcountry, check in with the park rangers for the current rules about lighting a fire at your campsite. If the area is especially dry, it may not be allowed.

Matches or Lighters? Most backpackers carry a lighter because it can get a campfire going and also light their stoves for making dinner. Lighters are inexpensive, lightweight, and easy to use, but bring matches as a backup, especially if you're going far from civilization.

CONTINUED ON NEXT PAGE!

2. COLLECT SOME FIREWOOD.
You'll need twigs, dry leaves, or needles to serve as tinder, small sticks for kindling, and larger pieces of wood as your main source of fuel. You can typically find them all within easy walking distance of your campsite.

Car campers, on the other hand, may have the luxury of purchasing a supply of wood prior to entering the campgrounds, saving time and energy in the process.

3. START STACKING.
Whether you create a wooden pyramid (kindling standing up on their ends and leaning against one another) or you employ the "log cabin" method (setting two pieces of wood alongside one another in a parallel fashion, then adding two more on top running perpendicular to the original sticks), the next steps are the same:

Add tinder inside the structure you just made and set it ablaze. Because tinder is small, it should ignite quickly and easily, transferring the heat and flame to the larger sticks, which in time will also catch on fire.

As the fire grows in size, slowly add some of the larger pieces of wood. These should burn for a longer period of time and at a hotter temperature.

From there, simply add more firewood as needed until you're ready to call it a night.

4. WHEN YOU'RE DONE WITH YOUR FIRE FOR THE EVENING, extinguish it by dousing it with water. Don't just assume it'll die down. Be sure it is out.

Eatin' Good in the Outdoors
CAMP STOVES
Thanks to small, light, and powerful camp stoves, it's easier than ever to make tasty meals at the campsite.

Backpackers should opt for small and efficient options. Car campers can get away with as much as they want to throw in the back of the vehicle.

The other determining factor is the type of fuel. Most camp stoves use gas or liquid fuel, with some using both. Gas typically comes in an easy-to-use pressurized fuel canister and provides a hot, efficient flame. Liquid fuel is usually white gas or kerosene and attaches to the stove through a refillable bottle. Multi-burner car-camping stoves tend to use propane, which provides much more heat and power, albeit at the expense of added weight.

COOLERS
Technology has transformed the humble cooler, turning what had been a simple vessel to hold ice, food, and cold drinks into unbreakable containers that keep ice cold for days at a time. This gives campers the option to bring more fresh fruits, vegetables, and meats with us without fear that they will spoil within a day or two.

Carrying a cooler into the backcountry isn't an option for backpackers, but car campers can spoil themselves.

BEAR WITH ME
Taking care of your food and trash at the campsite is crucial. Wild animals are not shy about looking for food and will wander into the area if they think they can get a handout. It is not uncommon for them to go through your backpack, cooler, trash, or car in search of leftovers.

If you're camping in bear country:

> Cook your meals at least 200 feet away from where you'll be sleeping.

> Before turning in for the night, stash your food somewhere safe that is equally far away.

> Many campers put their food in a backpack or bag and suspend it from a tree using a rope to keep it out of reach. Others will carry a bear canister to help keep ursine intruders at bay.

Bears aren't the only menace. Raccoons, marmots, mice, and other small animals have been known to pilfer tasty morsels when given the chance. Hanging your food tends to keep it out of reach for these creatures, too.

If your campsite has trash cans, secure the lids as tightly as possible. That will help to keep scraps and other waste secure. Of course, be sure to clean up and carry out all of your trash when you leave camp, adhering to the leave no trace policies.

Let's Turn In
SLEEPING BAGS
Every sleeping bag is rated for a certain temperature. Camp in colder conditions and you run the risk of finding yourself uncomfortably chilly. So know the conditions you'll be sleeping in.

The other factor to consider is the shape. Traditional sleeping bags are rectangular in shape, which tends to be less confining but also less efficient when it comes to trapping heat inside. Alternatively, mummy bags wrap snugly around the body, including the head, to generate more warmth. The narrow fit of a mummy bag can restrict movement, making it more difficult to get a proper night's sleep. Many people find them claustrophobic.

Modern sleeping bags come with natural down insulation or a synthetic option. Down has the best warmth-to-weight ratio of any insulation but loses some of its gusto if it gets wet. The introduction of hydrophobic down has diminished this concern, eliminating the major benefit that synthetic insulation had going for it. That said, today's synthetic insulation is warm, efficient, and lightweight.

SLEEPING PADS

A sleeping pad is an inflatable mattress that protects the camper from the stiffness and moisture of the hard ground. With these, you want to think about R-value, a measurement of an insulating material's ability to resist the transfer of heat. A higher R-value indicates better insulating properties, which is important when sleeping on the cold ground.

HAMMOCKS

Hammocks have taken off as a much more viable alternative to sleeping bags in recent years, thanks in no small part to better gear. Replace your tent with a hammock and you could save weight in your backpack while gaining a more soothing night's sleep.

Everything Else You Need

LIGHTING YOUR WAY

Lights: While the classic Coleman Lantern remains a viable option, modern lanterns are brighter, more efficient, and more capable. Opt for a lightweight one that has an easy-to-use brightness dial, rechargeable batteries, and has a good hanging mechanism.

Head Lamps: They're great for hiking and practical for finding your way around camp in the dark without carrying a flashlight.

PLEASE BE SEATED

For Backpackers: Minimalist chairs have shrunk so much that now backpackers who never would have considered adding a chair to their pack can do so.

For Weekend Warriors: A car camper should always take a camping chair to the site. Not only is it easy enough to pack, but it will make your camping trip much more comfortable.

PORTABLE POWER

It's easy to find as much recharging power as you need, from compact battery packs built for overnighters in the backcountry, to large portable stations that can power lights, small appliances, and other electronics.

Now Get Out There!

Whew! That's a lot to take in, but setting up your campsite sounds more challenging than it actually is. After you've done it a time or two, it won't seem nearly as daunting. Practicing in your own backyard is always a great way to get prepared. The most important thing is to enjoy your time outdoors and make your camping excursions as comfortable as possible. The rewards for doing just that will be numerous.

Rube Goldberg Machine

Will your machine help you brush your teeth, feed your dog, light a fire, or catapult a ball? Get your creative juices flowing!

Why It Matters

Rube Goldberg was well known for his creative concoctions to solve everyday tasks. Many of his designs triggered chain reactions that were widely considered to be delightfully fun, especially when a simple task was made more complex. Use all parts of the engineering design process to create your own machine. What will your machine do?

1. Decide What Your Machine Will Do. The first step in the engineering design process is to define your problem. Yes, we're building a Rube Goldberg machine, but what do you want it to do? Will it rain confetti or create a splash of paint or water at the end?

2. Brainstorm. Once you've decided on the final trigger piece for your big finale, figure out how you're going to get there. How do you want it to look? You can be as elaborate as you want, but sometimes a simple, but solid, structure is just as impressive!

3. Think About Materials. Will it include marble runs, knock over dominoes, or have swinging objects that play music like a pendulum? Consider magnets, rubber bands, paper cups, toy cars, balloons, dominoes, marble run pieces, tissues, string, pulleys, cardboard, tinfoil, plastic water bottles, fans, PVC pipe, box tape, water, bowls, and wooden blocks. The possibilities are endless!

4. Pull in Science and Math. Consider what you've learned about energy stores and transference, as well as speed and friction.

a. Does your machine start on a level platform and then trigger reactions to move the energy up or down?

b. Does that decrease or increase the speed of your pathway?

c. Do the weight of the materials play a factor?

d. How fast will the object be going and when will friction or wind resistance eventually slow it down?

e. Do you have another trigger item like a magnet, rubber band, or hammer that can store and release more energy to keep it going?

TIP

Consider marbles to help put your machine in motion. A marble sliding down a marble run may raise or lower the load, affecting the speed.

CONTINUED ON NEXT PAGE!

Rube Goldberg Machine

5. Sketch and Make Notes. It may help to provide reasoning or possible solutions for troubleshooting when things don't go as planned. For example, does wood or plastic change the speed of a marble run? Perhaps the incline or slope will need to be adjusted, or even the weight of the object, if working with a zipline. Does your Rube Goldberg machine play music? Is there enough tension in the strings or weight to band a drum and then trigger a catapult?

6. Build Your Prototype. Lay out all of your materials and decide how you can connect them together to create chain reactions where needed. Remember:

a. Pushes and pulls can have a dramatic effect when integrating magnets and pendulums.

b. Implement some math to get the right angles and lengths of materials in your trial runs.

c. Engineers of Rube Goldberg machines often have to run many trials to get the timing and adjustments just right for the machine to get all the chain reactions to work effectively. That's the iteration step to get the best machine possible!

7. Make It Look Appealing. The science and math are great, but pulling in technology, art, and engineering skills are key to making both creating and watching it work truly enjoyable.

a. Will you make colorful ribbons fly in the wind created by using a fan as an energy source?

b. Will you line your marble run with conductive copper tape? Consider that you can connect alligator clips to the back of a pegboard. Behind the pegboard is a circuit board secured with zip ties and connected to a computer. Will you code so that when the marble hits a certain point on the tape it triggers a sound?

c. Will *you* be a part of your machine? Will you include a hobby or passion like sports, STEAM, cooking, music, or reading?

Take It One Step Further

It can take a long time to set up a machine that runs in less than a minute between trials. You may wish to film your process to view later and help you troubleshoot. Using the slo-mo feature on a phone or camera lets you see the machine in action and observe and measure the chain reactions over a longer time frame. Share your final product, maybe even on a blog! You will be helping another fellow engineer in their preparations!

MAKE IT!
Robot Scribbler

Build a machine that draws on its own using markers and vibration. Guide the scribbler with your hand or let it go and see what it creates.

Why It Matters

Robots are machines that can be programmed to perform tasks. They are given a set of algorithms to complete jobs required in many factories and industries. By applying some engineering skills with soldering and woodworking, and then adding in some basic circuitry and a little math, you can create your first robot!

What You'll Need

1 cedar board (1- x 6-inch)

1 scrap board (1- x 2-inch)

1 Uxcell mini-vibration vibrating motor 2,750 rpm DC 1.5-6V

1 CR-2032 battery holder

1 CR-2032 battery

Hot-glue gun

2 rubber bands

Wood glue

120-grit sandpaper

Washable markers

3½-inch holesaw

Drill

Compass

Miter saw, jigsaw, or handsaw and miter box

Clamps

$^{13}\!/_{64}$-inch twist drill bit

Soldering iron

1. Use a 3½-inch holesaw in a drill press or a cordless drill to cut out two wood discs (Fig. A) from the 1- x 6-inch cedar.

2. Draw a centered 2½-inch circle on each disc with a compass. This will help you align the holes for the markers.

3. Sand the edges of the cut discs smooth using 120-grit sandpaper.

4. Using a miter saw, jigsaw, or a handsaw and miter box, crosscut the scrap block to 1½ inches long. Spread wood glue on the end-grain of the block, center it between the two discs, and clamp the pieces together to dry (Fig. B).

5. On the top disc, make six equidistant marks on the perimeter of the 2½-inch circle you drew. Space the marks about $^{13}\!/_{16}$ inches apart, but there's no need to be exact.

6. Use a drill with a $^{13}\!/_{64}$-inch twist drill bit to make a hole on each mark, passing the bit through the upper and lower discs.

CONTINUED ON NEXT PAGE!

Robot Scribbler

7. Solder the leads from the vibrating motor to the battery holder. Glue the battery holder and motor to the upper disc with hot glue (Fig. C).

8. Install the battery, then slip a piece of paper between the battery and the contacts to break the connection.

9. Insert colored markers in the holes and hold them in place by looping two rubber bands around them (Fig. D). Remove the paper from under the battery holder and set the bot down on a piece of paper to create your masterpiece.

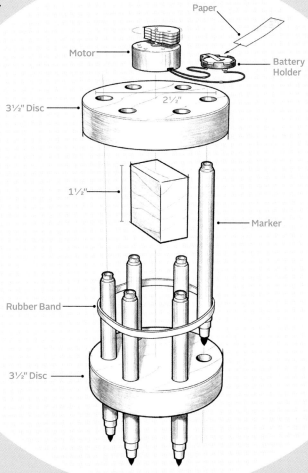

Paper

Motor

Battery Holder

3½" Disc

2½"

1½"

Marker

Rubber Band

3½" Disc

MAKE IT!

Air Hockey Table

Because the proper bank shot is a skill for life.

Why It Matters

The playing platform of an air hockey table isn't simply a piece of wood. You need the science and technology skills of aerodynamics, circuitry, and pushes and pulls found in magnetism to make it work. Add in the right air flow and air pressure to make the puck levitate, and you might discover how hovercrafts work (maybe a project for another time?).

What You'll Need

2- x 4-feet dry-erase hobby board

⅛-inch x 2- x 4-foot piece hardboard

6 square poplar dowels (½- x 36-inch)

1 round poplar dowel (½- x 40-inch)

Piece of felt, approximately 7 x 4 inches

Electric fan (part No. 1238AXCF-115VAC120mm)

2-inch air hockey pucks (part No. 55120-UK2)

6 screws (1-inch, any type)

Package #18 x ¾-inch finishing nails

Piece ¾-inch scrap wood

1. Use a table saw or jigsaw to cut the dry erase board and hardboard to 24- x 15⅛-inches.

2. Create a ¾-inch grid pattern on the top of the dry-erase board with a permanent marker.

3. Place the dry-erase board face up on a piece of scrap wood. Use a $\frac{5}{64}$-inch bit to drill holes through the grid you just made.

4. Using a jigsaw with a fine-tooth blade, cut a 4½-inch-diameter hole on center in the hardboard.

5. Cut six 3-inch lengths from the round poplar dowel with a miter saw, and set two of the lengths aside. Attach the other four dowels 1 inch in from each corner of the bottom of the hardboard by drilling pilot holes, adding glue to the top of the dowel, and securing with 1-inch screws.

6. Cut two 24-inch lengths and two 14¹⁄₁₆-inch lengths from the square dowels. These will be the spacers between the hardwood and the dry erase surface. Use wood glue and clamps to secure the dowels along the perimeter of the bottom of the dry-erase board, then glue the hardboard to the other side of the spacers.

7. Cut two more 24-inch lengths from the square dowels, and four 5-inch lengths from the remaining scraps. These will form the boundary of the dry-erase board. Glue the pieces to the board, using the short dowels to create a goal opening on each end. Tack the dowels down with the small finishing nails.

CONTINUED ON NEXT PAGE!

Air Hockey Table

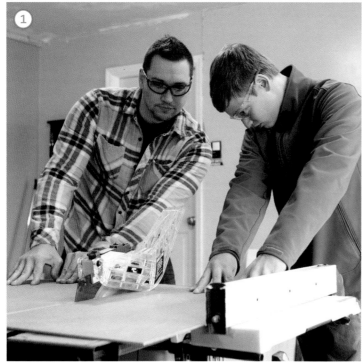

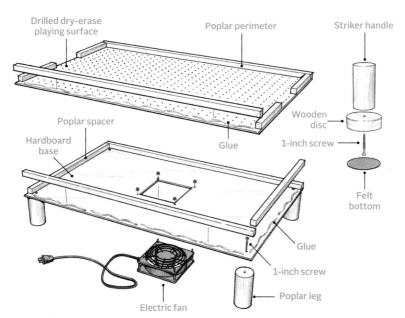

Drilled dry-erase playing surface

Poplar perimeter

Striker handle

Poplar spacer

Hardboard base

Glue

Wooden disc

1-inch screw

Felt bottom

Glue

1-inch screw

Poplar leg

Electric fan

8. Using the provided screws, attach the fan and shroud to the bottom of the hardboard to direct airflow to the playing surface.

9. To create the striker, use a 2 ½-inch holesaw to cut two discs from a ¾-inch-thick piece of scrap wood. Attach the remaining 3-inch sections of round dowel to the discs with glue. Drill pilot holes and fasten with 1-inch screws. Cut the felt (use the discs for size) and glue to the bottom of the striker.

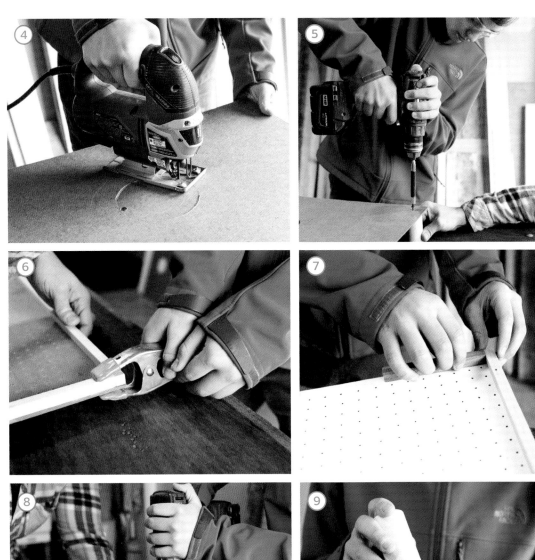

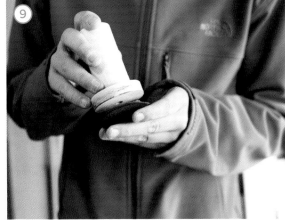

MAKE IT!

Steerable Sled

There's nothing like the whoosh of the wind as you go downhill on a sled!

Why It Matters

This is a basic design to get you started. The science behind the build takes into account the weight of the sled, the weight of the people riding in it, the slope of the hill you will go down, and the materials for the movement required. Want something built for speed? While smooth plastic on the underside makes for a very fast surface, rubbing some paraffin wax on it will really make it fly!

What You'll Need

- ¾- x 1½-inch x 8-feet PVC trim board
- 2 select studs (2- x 4 inches x 8 feet)
- ⅜- x 3½-inch carriage bolt and nut
- 3 galvanized steel washers (⅜ inch)
- 1-lb box No.10 2½-inch deck screws
- 6-feet piece of ⅜-inch nylon rope
- ½- x 8- x 12-inch poplar board (home centers will cut to length) or scrap plywood
- ½- x 8- x 12-inch poplar board (home centers will cut to length) or ¾-inch plywood (seat)
- 2- x 4- x 30-inch Hem-fir board (center support)
- 2 Hem-fir boards (2 x 4 x 18 inches) (crossarm, steering arm)
- 4 Hem-fir boards (2 x 4 x 18 inches) (runners)
- 4 PVC trim (¾ x 1½ x 24 inches) (runner face)

1. Measure and mark the 2 x 4s and the PVC trim to prepare them for crosscutting. Remember to mark an X on the scrap side of the line.

2. Crosscut the 2 x 4s and the PVC trim to length by cutting on the scrap side. If you have a scrap piece of plywood, cut the seat from it. Otherwise you can buy a short piece of poplar.

3. Use a six-teeth-per-inch woodcutting blade in a jigsaw to cut the 30-degree angle end on the runners.

4. Mark a line across the PVC trim at 10 inches and clamp it firmly in a vise at the line. Pull the PVC toward you to bend it at an angle just greater than 30 degrees, so that when the PVC springs back slightly you'll get an exact fit. You can always use the runner to check the angle.

5. Mark the center of the steering arm and bore a ½-inch-diameter hole through it. Bore two ½-inch holes for the towrope, approximately 3 inches in from each end of the steering arm.

6. Screw the PVC to the runners, then screw the steering arm and the rear crossarm to the runners. Screw the center support to the rear runner.

7. Bolt the steering arm to the center support and fasten the towrope through the holes on the arm by knotting them.

8. Knot the towrope in place and screw the seat to the center support.

CONTINUED ON NEXT PAGE!

SERVICE

12"   8"

24"

30"

24"

18"

12"

24" total
length

Take It One Step Further

Use the engineering design process to iterate an even better-working design to increase your speed and distance traveled! Will you add any technology like a pedometer, compass, or phone to track the distance you cross at different speeds and inclines? Will you try using wheels, tennis rackets, or something else to glide across the snow more easily? Maybe a different base—foam, wood, plastic, etc.—will affect friction and increase resistance? Test it out and see if you come up with a new design!

Steerable Sled

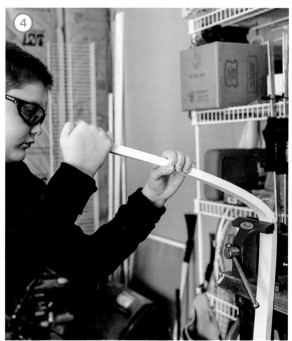

FUN FACT

Egyptians built the world's first paved road. Workers later added wooden tracks and sleds to haul stones from the quarries to early construction sites, which eventually helped build the pyramids.

Adult Supervision Required!

MAKE IT!
Marble Run

The clatter will eventually drive you nuts, but this magnetic marble run is infinitely reconfigurable—and a lot of fun!

Why It Matters

Magnets allow you to reposition and repurpose the marble run to be used over and over again. Use math and science to determine just the right shape and angles to keep the marble from falling off the track. Determining tilt and taking advantage of force of gravity will affect speed. Even with this basic design, there's a lot of variables to play with. Who knows? Maybe you'll get inspired to build a rollercoaster next!

What You'll Need

- 1 quarter sheet of ¼-inch birch plywood
- 1 pkg. (40 pcs) button magnets
- 1 bottle carpenter's glue or craft adhesive
- 1 bag marbles
- 60-, 80-, and 120-grit sandpaper

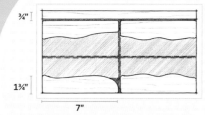
¾"
1¾"
7"

After you cut a ¾-inch strip off the plywood, the rest should be used to design shapes for the marble run.

1. After an adult rips a ¾-inch-wide strip from the plywood, use the rest for drawing ramp shapes—straight lines, rolling curves, ski jumps. Be sure to make one that has a lip on both ends. This piece will catch the marbles at the bottom of each run.

2. Clamp the plywood to a workbench and use a jigsaw and a curve-cutting blade to cut out the ramp shapes. Smooth off any rough edges of the pieces using 80- and 120-grit sandpaper.

3. Crosscut the ¾-inch-wide strip into spacer blocks, which will go behind your ramp pieces. Using a simple and inexpensive hand miter saw (such as the Stanley 20-600, pictured on the next page) enables younger woodworkers to participate.

4. Glue two spacer blocks and magnets to the back of each ramp. You can use more for larger pieces. Be sure that the blocks are glued so that they don't project out over the edge of the ramp and interfere with the marble as it rolls.

5. Place a board and a weight of some kind on top of each ramp and the spacer blocks to provide pressure and a better glue bond. Allow the glue to dry for a few hours.

6. Bevel the back edge of each ramp using 60- and 80-grit sandpaper wrapped around a block of wood, or use a rubber sanding block. The beveled edge provides a secure track for the marble to roll in.

CONTINUED ON NEXT PAGE!

Take It One Step Further

Build on this design by adding hidden features for the marble to pass through. Add different mediums like textured paint or finishing sprays to lessen or increase the amount of friction. You can even trigger an event at the end and incorporate a little technology—maybe a buzzer switch with a battery in a container at the bottom? Get creative!

Marble Run

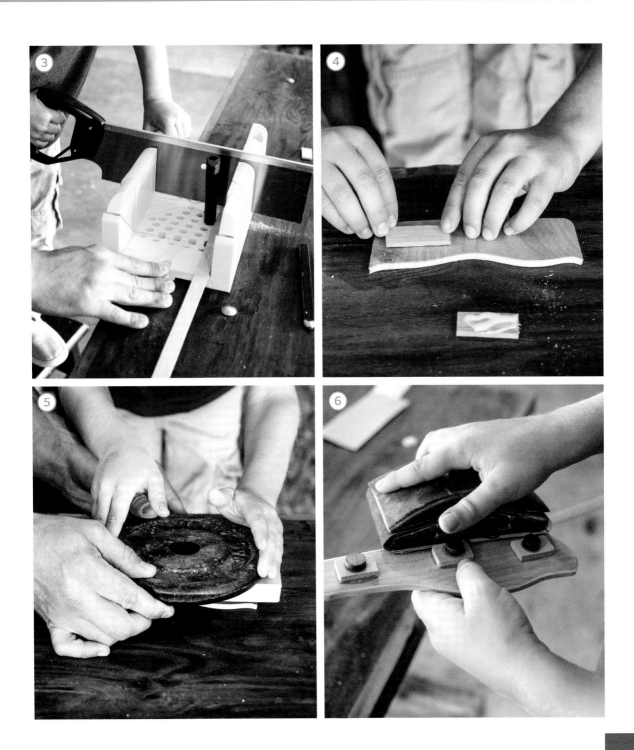

Six Things to Remember Now That You're Done!

What a journey! By now, you should know how to use the engineering process and maker mindset to work through any obstacles with creativity, authenticity, and tenacity. As you go on making, keep these things in mind:

1 Reflection is an Integral Part of STEAM

When you hit a bump in the road, don't be afraid to take a break. Calm down and collect your thoughts, critically think through the problem, and then create again.

2 New Experiences Inspire New Ideas

Go for a stroll in the park. Take a road trip to a different city. Try something you've never done before. Who knows what you might discover? Most importantly, you'll gain a new perspective.

3 Just Because It Hasn't Been Done Doesn't Mean You Shouldn't Do It

Your STEAM journey may take you down many different paths. Don't worry if you go off the beaten trail. Sometimes, that's where the magic happens.

4 It's Okay to Change Your Mind as You Go

Course corrections provide new perspectives that can entirely change your invention for the better. When roadblocks appear, use them as stepping stones to get you where you want to go. Work through the problem with your STEAM tool kit.

5 All True Makers and Inventors Fail

And often many times before they succeed! But they NEVER give up. What about you? Are you brave? We hope so!

6 Always Take One Last Look

Before you blow the world's mind with your final product, pause. Is there anything you missed that you need to go back and work through? Did you test your prototype many times to make sure it works properly? Do you need to iterate and improve it? Put out the best product you can, but only after you reflect to make it the best it can possibly be!

That's the engineering design process at work!

So... what will *you* invent or make? How will you transform the world through STEAM to leave it better than you found it? We wish you the very best on what will become a very gratifying journey indeed. We can't wait to see what you engineer and make!

Solutions

Plants' Defense Mechanisms

Answer Key to Thorny Plants

1. True - Due to the need for nitrogen required for plant cell growth.

2. False - A holly bush's thorn alternates between pointing upward and downward.

3. True - This is one of their many adaptations.

4. False - Bougainvillea sap is known to cause a significant skin rash called dermatitis due to its mild toxins. Stay away from it!

5. True - Other plants are not a fan as they get used and abused to support the crown of thorns! It's deadly to other animals too. The sap from broken branches leaking into ponds is known to kill fish!

The Ideal Temperature for Hot Chocolate
Pg 27

194°F Serving Temperature	-	66°F Room Temperature	=	128°F Temperature Difference
128°F Temperature Difference	/	2 Minutes	=	64 Half-life
66°F Room Temperature	+	64 Half-life	=	130°F Hot cocoa temperature after 2 minutes

One Light, Three Switches
Pg 36

Flip switch number one and wait a few minutes. Flip switch number one back to its original position, and then immediately flip switch number two.

Open the door. If the light is on, then switch number two controls it. If the light is off, then go and feel the bulb with your hand. If the bulb is hot, then switch number one controls it, and if the bulb is cool, then switch number three, the one you did not touch, controls it.

Rock-Paper-Scissors Riddle
Pg 56

Let's look at the played hands again:
Jack: 3 rock, 6 scissors, 1 paper
Jill: 2 rock, 4 scissors, 4 paper

The key to solving this riddle is realizing that Jack played scissors six times. Because there were no ties, that means Jill didn't play scissors in any of those six games. Now look at the various hands Jill did play. Because she played scissors four times, and none of those could've lined up with one of the six times Jack played scissors, she must have played all six of her other hands on Jack's six scissors.

Therefore, six of the games, not necessarily in order, were as follows:

Jack: scissors vs. Jill: rock [Winner: Jill]
Jack: scissors vs. Jill: rock [Winner: Jill]
Jack: scissors vs. Jill: paper [Winner: Jack]
Jack: scissors vs. Jill: paper [Winner: Jack]
Jack: scissors vs. Jill: paper [Winner: Jack]
Jack: scissors vs. Jill: paper [Winner: Jack]

Now look at what is left over. We see that Jill has only scissors left. Therefore, the other four games are:

Jack: rock vs. Jill: scissors [Winner: Jack]
Jack: rock vs. Jill: scissors [Winner: Jack]
Jack: rock vs. Jill: scissors [Winner: Jack]
Jack: paper vs. Jill: scissors [Winner: Jill]

Tally it all up and Jack wins, seven to three.

The Locker Prank
Pg 57

1, 4, 9, 16, 25, 36, 49, 64, 81, 100
// Every locker will have its status changed by a student with a number that is a factor of that locker number. (Locker 24 will be opened/closed by students 1, 2, 3, 4, 6, 8, 12, and 24.) Lockers with an odd number of factors will ultimately remain open, and lockers with factors that are a pair (16, with 4 and 4, for example) are the only ones with an odd number of factors. Those lockers are also perfect squares. Only locker numbers that are perfect squares are left open.

Mathematical Life Skills
Pg 66

Leaving a Tip: $25.46

Baking Cookies:
1 cup flour = ⅔ cup flour
¾ cup sugar = ½ cup sugar
½ cup butter = ⅓ cup butter
1½ cups chocolate chips = 1 cup chocolate chips
1 teaspoon pure vanilla extract = ⅔ teaspoon pure vanilla extract

Splitting an Uber:
$2.70 (cost per mile) x 4.5 (distance) = $12.15
$12.15 + $2.60 (base rate) = $14.75
$14.75 x 1.2 (tip) = $17.70
$17.70 / 4 (people sharing the ride) = $4.43 (rounded up from $4.425)

Ordering Pizza:
10″ - 2″ (crust) = 8″
15″ - 2″ (crust) = 13″
$10 / 8 = $1.25
$15 / 13 = $1.15

The better value:
The 15-inch pizza gives you more for less cost.

Upcycled Art
Pg 78

1. This is true, as long as you cut off the zipper portion of it.

2. This is not true. Soda cans don't need to be in good condition to be recycled.

3. This is true. It can be dangerous to throw old electronics in recycling because they might have lithium batteries that can explode and catch fire.

4. This is false. Plastic bags pose a lot of problems for sorting facilities. Instead, put them in a separate bin and throw them in plastic bags-specific recycling bins at school.

5. This is false. Steel and tin cans can save 60 to 74 percent of the energy needed to make new ones from raw materials. Aluminum cans can save 95 percent.

The Lowdown on Dams
Pg 104

1. Ashfork-Bainbridge Dam

2. Theodore Roosevelt Dam

3. Grand Coulee Dam

4. 21 billion kilowatt-hours of electricity annually

5. Fort Peck Dam

6. The Hoover Dam

7. Glen Canyon

8. Encourages fewer droughts for those living downstream while reserving water runoff for years with less rainfall

9. Oroville Dam

10. Dworshak Dam

Credits

Credits

DIMITRI OTIS/GETTY IMAGES: 118;

JUSTIN PAGET/GETTY IMAGES: 188;

GABRIEL PEREZ/GETTY IMAGES: 23 middle;

BETH PERKINS: 116;

PHOTOGRAPHED BY RANDI ANG/ GETTY IMAGES: 102 bottom right;

PHOTO MIO JAPAN/GETTY IMAGES: 189 top right;

P_PONOMAREVA/ISTOCK/GETTY IMAGES PLUS: 143;

RAPIDEYE/ISTOCK/GOOGLE IMAGES PLUS: 38 top;

YULIA REZNIKOV/GETTY IMAGES: 185;

BARBARA RICH/GETTY IMAGES: 102 bottom left;

SASKIA RISCHKA/EYEEM/GETTY IMAGES: 23 top right;

ROCKSUNDERWATER/ISTOCK/ GOOGLE IMAGES PLUS: 26 left;

SCKREPKA/ISTOCK/GETTY IMAGES PLUS: 20 top;

SCULDER19/ISTOCK/GOOGLE IMAGES PLUS: 42;

SEVENTYFOUR/ISTOCK/GOOGLE IMAGES PLUS: 45 bottom;

TERESA SHORT/GETTY IMAGES: 145;

JUSTIN SMITH/ISTOCK/GETTY IMAGES PLUS: 36;

SOLSTOCK/GOOGLE IMAGES: 45 top;

LAURA BOLOKOSKI STEED/ISTOCK/ GETTY IMAGES PLUS: 14 bottom right;

MARCIA STRAUB/GETTY IMAGES: 112;

KANPOB SUWANNASOOK/EYEEM/ GOOGLE IMAGES: 56;

DANIELA SIMONA TEMNEANU/ EYEEM/GETTY IMAGES: 136 left;

TERRYFIC3D/ISTOCK/GETTY IMAGES PLUS: 102 top;

TETSUOMORITA/GETTY IMAGES: 38 bottom;

THENOUNPROJECT: STEAM category icons and Adult Supervision icon;

WESTEND61/GETTY IMAGES: 119;

ROBERT WINKLER/ISTOCK/GETTY IMAGES PLUS: 14 top right;

WRAGG/ISTOCK/GOOGLE IMAGES PLUS: 50;

ALAN V. YOUNG/GETTY IMAGES: 156;

REED YOUNG: 174-177;

ZIMINDMITRY/ISTOCK/GETTY IMAGES: 30 top left

Illustration

LANA BRAGINA: 52;

JOHN BURGOYNE: 100;

ALEX GRIENDLING: 150, 176;

VIC KULIHAN: 41;

MARTIN LAKSMAN: 30, 33, 37, 58-61, 73, 93, 125, 171, 181;

JEFFREY LOWRY: 13, 63;

GILLIAN MACLEOD: 122;

DIEGO MORALES: 173;

LIEF PARSONS: 107, 159;

CHRIS PHILPOT: 18-19, 46-47, 54-55, 74, 99, 185;

GEORGE RETSECK: 82, 88, 110, 115, 121, 127-139, 155, 160-168, 203-212

Activity Design

KRAIG BECKER: 190-195;

JAY BENNET: 36, 56;

ROY BERENDSOHN: 88-92, 110;

LESTER BLACK: 144-145;

THERESA BREEN: 170-171, 178-181;

WAYNE COFFEY: 60-61;

CAROLINE DELBERT: 66-69, 74;

MICHELE ERVIN: 40-41, 93;

LAURA FEIVESON: 57;

HAYLEY GLATTER: 80-81;

MATT GOULET: 16;

MARY BETH GRIGGS: 30-31;

MARY GRUBER: 21, 22 (True or False), 28, 34, 39, 42-43, 48-49, 52-53, 62-65, 75, 79, 86-87, 99, 100-101 (Engineering A Sailboat Powered by Wind), 104-105 (Trivia Questions), 113, 118, 122-123, 140-143, 146-147, 156-157, 184-189, 197-198;

WILLIAM GURSTELLE: 94-95, 149-150, 172;

SARAH HANSEN: 37;

TED KILCOMMONS: 168-169;

COURTNEY LINDER: 77-78;

JAMES LYNCH: 50-51;

ROBERT MORITZ: 70-73;

ROBERT AND MARIGOLD MORITZ: 124-125;

JENNIFER NALEWICKI: 25;

TIM NEWCOMB: 58-59, 103-104 (The Lowdown on Dams);

POPULAR MECHANICS EDITORS: 12-15, 26-27, 96-98, 101 (How Wind Moves a Boat), 117;

POPULAR MECHANICS EDITORS AND ETHAN, SEAMUS, AND BEN DONALDSON: 174-177;

JAMES SCHADEWALD: 82-85, 114-115, 120-121, 126-138, 152-155, 160-167, 200-215;

ALYSON SHEPPARD: 32-33;

JOHN RIHA: 22 (A Field Guide to Thorny Plants);

JOSEPH TRUINI: 25, 44-45;

BRUCE YEANY: 158-159